CAMELOT

Music by
FREDERICK LOEWE

Book and Lyrics by
ALAN JAY LERNER

Based on
The Once and Future King
by T. H. WHITE

Vocal Score

$25.00

Edited by Franz Allers
Piano Reduction by Trude Rittman

CHAPPELL MUSIC COMPANY

CAMELOT

Produced by the Messrs. LERNER · LOEWE · HART
December 3, 1960 at the Majestic Theatre, New York City

Production Staged by
MOSS HART

Choreography and Musical Numbers by HANYA HOLM
Scenic Production by OLIVER SMITH
Costumes Designed by ADRIAN, AND TONY DUQUETTER
Lighting by FEDER
Musical Direction by FRANZ ALLERS
Orchestrations by ROBERT RUSSELL BENNETT AND PHILIP J. LANG
Dance and Choral Arrangements by TRUDE RITTMAN
Hair Styles by ERNEST ADLER

Cast of Characters
(In order of appearance)

SIR DINADAN	John Cullum
SIR LIONEL	Bruce Yarnell
MERLYN	David Hurst
ARTHUR	Richard Burton
GUENEVERE	Julie Andrews
NIMUE	Marjorie Smith
A PAGE	Leland Mayforth
LANCELOT	Robert Goulet
DAP	Michael Clarke-Laurence
PELLINORE	Robert Coote
CLARIUS	Richard Kuch
LADY ANNE	Christina Gillespie
A LADY	Leesa Troy
SIR SAGRAMORE	James Gannon
A PAGE	Peter de Vise
HERALD	John Starkweather
LADY CATHERINE	Virginia Allen
MORDRED	Roddy McDowall
SIR OZANNA	Michael Kermoyan
SIR GWILLIAM	Jack Dabdoub
MORGAN LE FEY	M'el Dowd
TOM	Robin Stewart

SINGERS: Joan August, Mary Sue Berry, Marnell Bruce, Judy Hastings, Benita James, Marjorie Smith, Shelia Swenson, Leesa Troy, Dorothy White, Frank Bouley, Jack Dabdoub, James Gannon, Murray Goldkind, Warren Hays, Paul Huddleston, Michael Kermoyan, Donald Maloof, Larry Mitchell, Paul Richards, John Taliaferro.

DANCERS: Virginia Allen, Judi Allinson, Laurie Archer, Carlene Carroll, Joan Coddington, Katia Geleznova, Adriana Keathley, Dawn Mitchell, Claudia Schroeder, Beti Seay, Jerry Bowers, Peter Deign, Randy Doney, Richard Englund, Richard Gain, Gene GeBauer, James Kirby, Richard Kuch, Joe Nelson, John Starkweather, Jimmy Tarbutton.

CAMELOT

Synopsis of Scenes

ACT I

SCENE 1: A Hilltop near Camelot
    A long time ago

SCENE 2: Near Camelot
    Immediately following

SCENE 3: Arthur's Study
    Five years later

SCENE 4: A Roadside near Camelot
    A few months later

SCENE 5: A Park near the Castle
    Immediately following

SCENE 6: A Terrace of the Castle
    A few weeks later

SCENE 7: The Tents outside the Jousting Field
    A few days later

SCENE 8: The Grandstand of the Field

SCENE 9: The Tents outside the Jousting Field
    Immediately following

SCENE 10: The Terrace
    Two years later

SCENE 11: The Corridor Leading to the Great Hall
    Immediately following

SCENE 12: The Great Hall
    Immediately following

ACT II

SCENE 1: The Castle Garden
    A few years later

SCENE 2: The Terrace
    A few weeks later

SCENE 3: Near the Forest of Morgan le Fey
    A few days later

SCENE 4: The Forest of Morgan le Fey
    Immediately following

SCENE 5: Corridor
    That night

SCENE 6: The Queen's Bedchamber
    Immediately following

SCENE 7: Camelot
    Several days later

SCENE 8: A Battlefield Near Joyous Gard
    A few weeks later

ORIGINAL INSTRUMENTATION: Flute/*Piccolo,* Oboe/*English Horn,* B♭ Clarinet, B♭ Clarinet/*E♭ Clarinet/Bass Clarinet/Flute,* Bassoon; 3 Horns, 3 Trumpets, 2 Trombones; 2 Percussion, Guitar/*Lute/Mandolin,* Harp; 10 Violins, 2 Violas, 2 Violoncellos, 2 Basses.

Musical Program

ACT I

No.		page
1.	Overture	5
2.	March	11
3.	I Wonder What the King Is Doing Tonight	15
4.	The Simple Joys of Maidenhood	23
5.	Camelot	32
6.	Guenevere's Welcome	40
7.	End of Scene — Reprise: Camelot	43
8.	Follow Me	47
9.	End of Study Scene	51
10.	C'est Moi	52
11.	The Lusty Month of May — *dance*	59
	— *song*	67
11a.	Pellinore's Entrance	82
12.	End of Scene	83
13.	Change of Scene	86
14.	How to Handle a Woman	87
15.	Tent Scene	95
16.	The Tumblers	97
17.	The Jousts	100
18.	Change of Scene	120
19.	Before I Gaze at You Again	121
20.	Finale — Act I	125

ACT II

21.	Entr'acte	134
22.	a. Madrigal	141
	b. If Ever I Would Leave You	143
23.	The Seven Deadly Virtues	149
24.	Change of Scene	154
25.	What Do the Simple Folk Do?	155
26.	The Enchanted Forest	172
27.	The Persuasion	178
28.	The Invisible Wall	184
29.	Change of Scene	189
30.	Corridor Scene	190
31.	Change of Scene and Incidental Music	191
32.	I Loved You Once in Silence	193
33.	Guenevere	199
34.	Battle Call	219
35.	Farewell	220
36.	Finale Ultimo	221
37.	Curtain Calls and Exit Music	230

CAMELOT
Overture

No. 1

FREDERICK LOEWE

Copyright © 1962 by Alan Jay Lerner and Frederick Loewe
Chappell & Co. Inc., New York, N.Y. Publisher and Owner of allied rights throughout the world
International Copyright Secured   ALL RIGHTS RESVERED   Printed in U.S.A.
Unauthorized copying, arranging, adapting, recording or public performance is an infringement of copyright.
Infringers are liable under the law.

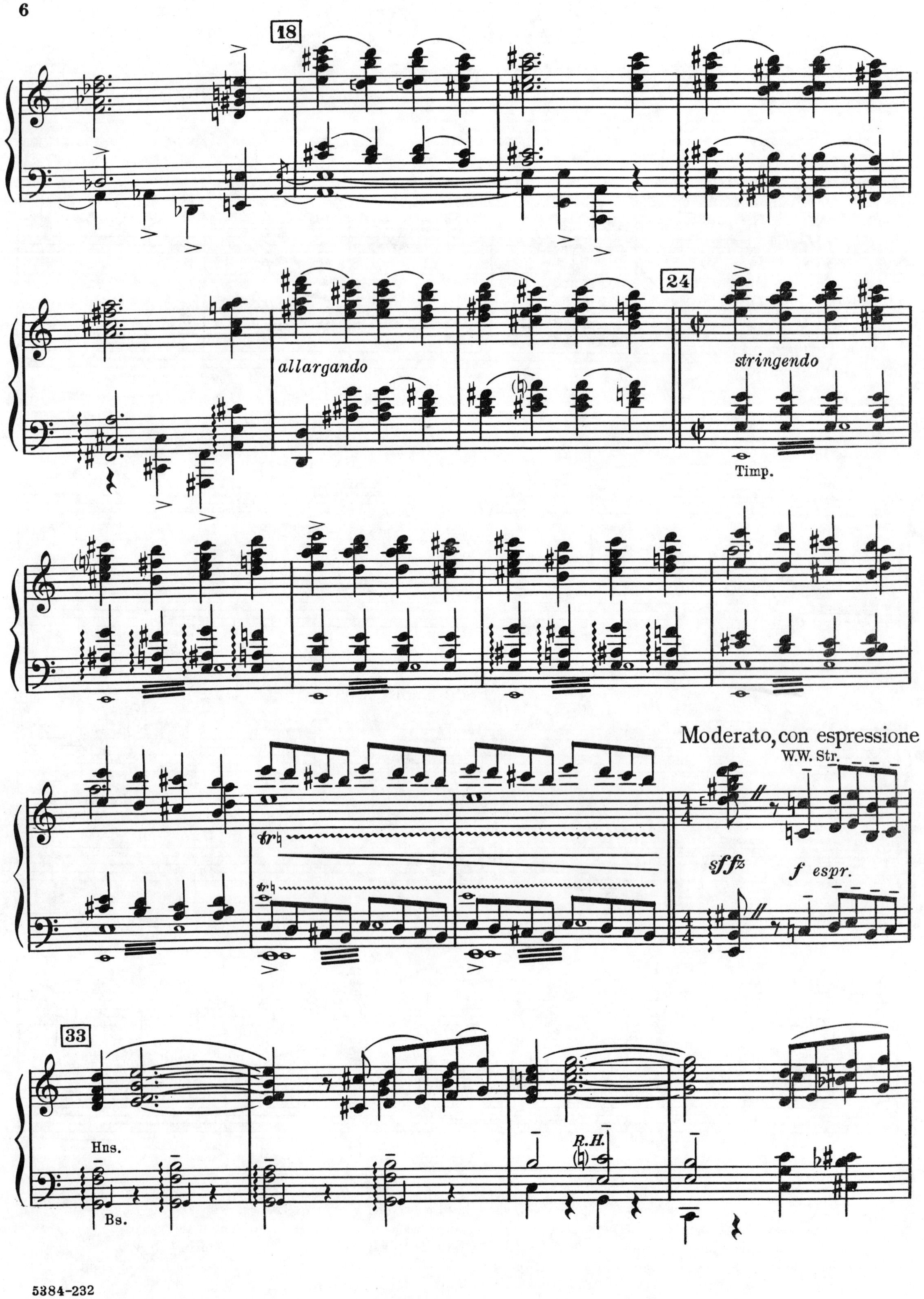
18
allargando
24
stringendo
Timp.
Moderato, con espressione
W.W. Str.
sffz
f espr.
33
Hns.
Bs.
R.H.

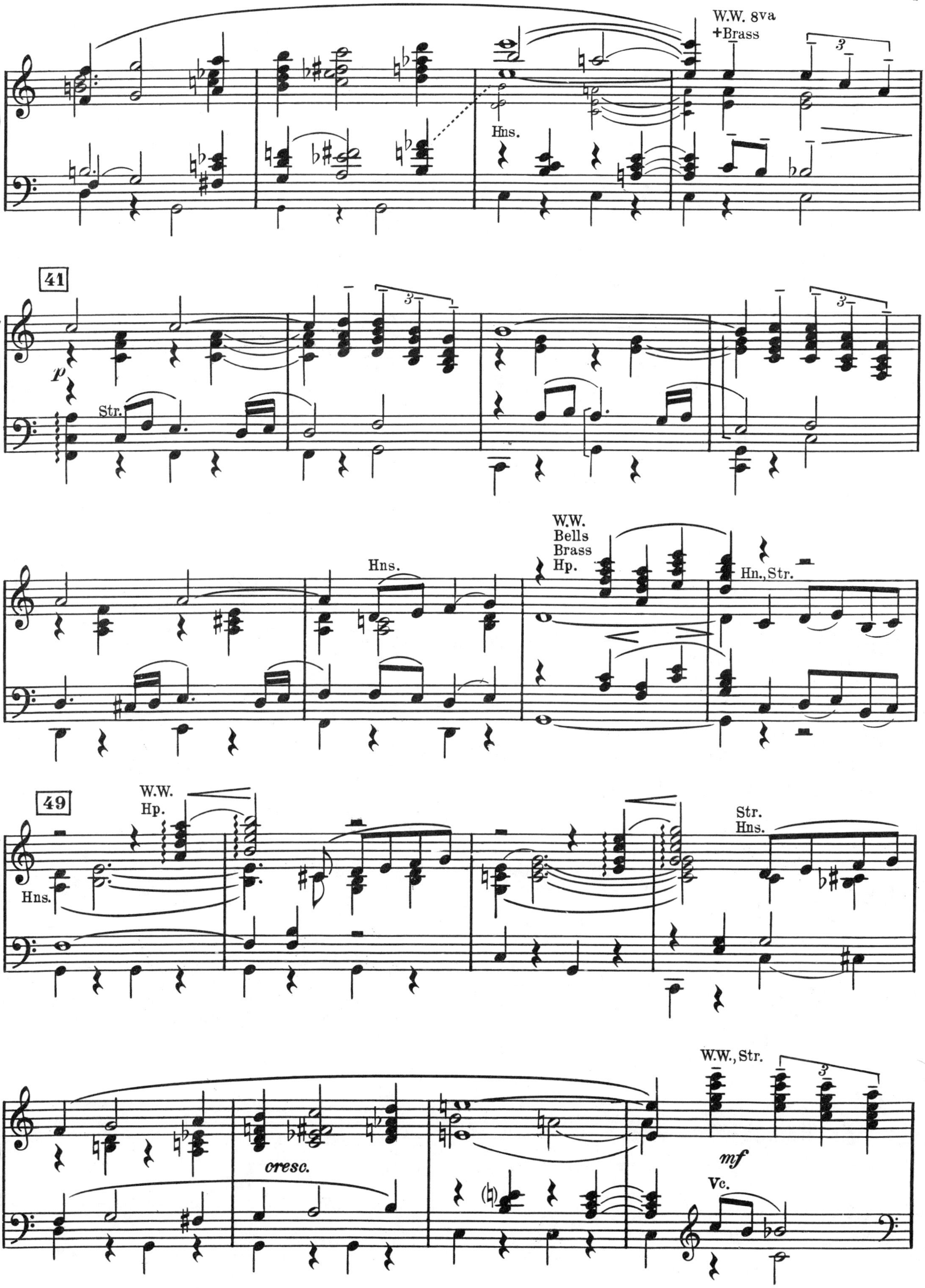
W.W. 8va
+Brass
Hns.
41
p
Str.
Hns.
W.W.
Bells
Brass
Hp.
Hn., Str.
49
W.W.
Hp.
Hns.
Str.
Hns.
cresc.
W.W., Str.
mf
Vc.

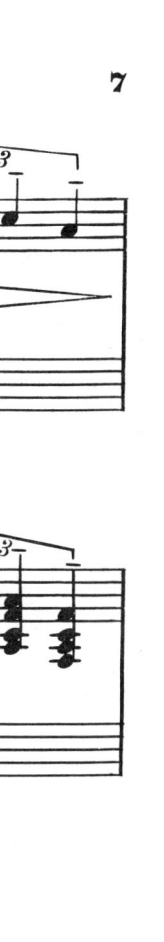

No. 2 March 11

Cue: SIR DINADAN:... at the foot of the hill in traditional fashion.

5384-232 Copyright © 1960 (unpub.) & 1962 by Alan Jay Lerner and Frederick Loewe

No. 3 I Wonder What The King Is Doing Tonight

ALAN JAY LERNER   **FREDERICK LOEWE**

Cue: ARTHUR: ... That's precisely what you are doing. Every last blessed one of you.

5384-232   Copyright © 1960 (unpub.) & 1962 by Alan Jay Lerner and Frederick Loewe

No. 4 The Simple Joys Of Maidenhood

Camelot

No. 5

Cue: ARTHUR: Ordained by decree!
...Extremely uncommon.
GUENEVERE: Oh, come now.

5384-232 Copyright © 1960 by Alan Jay Lerner and Frederick Loewe

49
Ca - me - lot,
Ca - me - lot,
That's
Ob.
Hns.
Str.
how con - di - tions are.
The
W.W.
Br. muted
Str.
57
rain may nev - er fall till aft - er sun - down.
By
W.W.
Hns.
Tpt.
eight the morn - ing fog must dis - ap - pear.
In
+Ob.
Tbs.

65
short, there's sim - ply not A more con - gen - ial spot For
Vc.
Poco meno mosso
happ'-ly-ev - er - aft - er - ing than here In
W.W. 8va
Str.
poco rit.
Bsn.
73
Tempo giusto
Ca - me - lot.
gliss.
accel.
Hp.
f Tutti leggiero sempre
79
GUENEVERE: And I suppose
Hp.
pp

the autumn leaves fall in neat little piles.
Hp.
Hns.
ARTHUR: Oh, no, Milady, they blow away completely.
87
Hn.
At night, of course.
Fls.
GUENEVERE: Of course!
Hns.
W.W., Str., Xyl.
f
He moves closer to her.
95
Ca - me - lot!
Tpt.
p
Hns.
Str.
Tbs.
W.W., Str., Xyl.
f
Ca - me - lot!
I know it gives a per - son pause,
W.W.
p
Hns.
Str.
mf
W.W.
Tpt.
f
Hns.

38

But in Ca - me - lot, Ca - me - lot, Those are the le - gal laws. The snow may nev - er slush up - on the hill - side. By nine p. m. the moon - light must ap-

119
pear.
In short, there's sim - ply not A
+Ob.
Tbs.
Vc.
more con - gen - ial spot For happ' - ly - ev - er - aft - er - ing than
poco rit.
125
Poco meno mosso
here in Ca - me -
Str.
W.W. 8va
accel.
129
Animato
lot.
Hns.
ff
Tpts.
W.W.
ff
Tutti
sfz
Segue

No. 6 Guenevere's Welcome

Cue: SIR DINADAN: There she is!
GUENEVERE: Wart, please....

17
f
p
mf
W.W., Str.
f
Hns.
25
cresc. Brass
Tutti
cantabile
espr.
ff sempre

cantabile
Hns., Str.
f Tutti
Bsn., Tbn., Vc., Bass
33
ben tenuto
W.W.
Bsn.
Hns.
Tbn.
W.W.
Tpts., Tbn.
dim. poco a poco
41
R.H.
Bsn.
Hn.
Vla.
Hp.
pizz.
Ob.
p
Bsn.
Dr.
Fl.
pp
(Dialogue)

No. 7 # End of Scene (Camelot Reprise)

Cue: ARTHUR: ... And since I am, I have been ill at ease in my crown. Until I dropped from the tree and my eyes beheld you.

Poco sostenuto

Then suddenly, for the first time, I felt I was King. I was glad to be King. And most astonishing of all, I wanted to be the wisest, most heroic, most splendid King who ever sat on any throne. *(He pauses)*

If you will come with me, Milady, I will arrange for the carriage to return you to your father... This way.

GUENEVERE: I

hear it never rains till after sundown. By eight the morning fog must disappear. In short, there's simply not A more congenial spot For happ'ly-ever-aftering than here In

41
Poco più mosso
Ca - me - lot.
Fl.
Cl.
Str.
amabile
mf
Hns.
Più mosso.
Str., Gtr.
mp
49
Hns.
pp
Bsn.
57
GUENEVERE: I'm afraid, Your Majesty. (Dialogue continues)
pp
Hp.
Cls.
Hp., Bells
Fl., Cl.
pp sempre
Fl.
Cl.
Hn.
Vla.

65
ARTHUR: ... War would have been declared.
73
GUENEVERE: War?
Vls.
+Gtr.
Vc.
Bsn.
Over me? How simply marvelous!
+W.W., Hns.
Allegro con spirito
W.W. Bells 8va
rit.
molto cresc.
Tbns.
Hp. gliss.
f a tempo
Tutti
81
brillante
W.W., Vls.
Bells 8va
Tpts.
Hns.
(Dialogue)
sffz

No. 8 — **Follow Me** — 47

Cue: MERLYN: ...One year... two years... what does it matter? I can see a night five years from now...

Andante

NIMUE'S VOICE: *(Offstage)*
Far from day, far from night... Out of time, out of sight...

SIR DINADAN: Go on. What about five years from now? MERLYN: Yes! After the battle of Bedegraine. That's the night it will happen!

Fol-low me... Dry the rain, warm the snow... Where the winds nev-er go...

SIR DINADAN: Go on. That's the night <u>what</u> will happen? MERLYN: I can't remember.

Più mosso

5384-232 Copyright © 1960 by Alan Jay Lerner and Frederick Loewe

That voice. Don't you hear it?
SIR DINADAN: What voice?
18
MERLYN: (over singing) Nimue,
Tempo I°
In a cave by a sap - phire
Vc.
Hp.
is that you?
Oh, please . . . .
not yet.
shore We shall walk through an em - 'rald door. And for
Hp., Bass
I must find out what will happen to him . . .
Con moto
thou-sands of ev - er - mores to come my life you shall be.
Vl. I
Str.
pp sempre
26
Oh, Nimue! So it's you! Must you steal my magic now? Couldn't you have waited a bit longer? . . . .
Hp., Vla.
Wait! Have I told him everything he should know?
Did I tell him of Lancelot? I did.
But Lancelot
+Fl.
ppp
p

49

home 'neath the sea We shall fly, Fol-low me.

home 'neath the sea We shall fly.

MERLYN: Goodbye, Arthur. My memory of the future is gone. I know no more the sorrows and joys before you

I can only wish for you in ignorance, like everyone else.

Reign long and reign happily.

Oh, and Wart — remember to think!

(Dialogue)

No. 9   End Of Study Scene

Cue: GUENEVERE: It's marvelous.
   ARTHUR: Yes, it is. It's marvelous. Absolutely marvelous. Page, give the signal.
   PAGE: Yes, your Majesty.

ARTHUR: We'll send the heralds riding through the country; Tell ev'ry living person far and near

GUENEVERE: That there is simply not In all the world a spot Where rules a more resplendant king than here

No. 10 — Countryside near Camelot.

C'est Moi

Vigoroso

Tempo rubato

LANCELOT: Ca - me - lot!___ Ca - me - lot! In far off France I heard your call.

53

Ca - me - lot! ... Ca - me - lot! ... And here am I to give my all. I know in my soul what you ex-pect of me; And

all that and more I shall be! A

33 Alla marcia

knight of the table round should be invincible; Such
soul of a knight should be a thing remarkable: His
ceed where a less fantastic man would fail; Climb a
heart and his mind as pure as morning dew. With a

41

wall no one else can climb; Cleave a dragon in record time; Swim a
will and a self-restraint That's the envy of ev'ry saint, He could

moat in a coat of heav-y i-ron mail. No
eas-i-ly work a mir-a-cle or two! To

49
mat-ter the pain he ought to be un-winc-a-ble, Im-
love and de-sire he ought to be un-spark-a-ble. The

poss-i-ble deeds should be his dai-ly fare. But
ways of the flesh should of-fer no al-lure. But

57
where in the world Is there in the world A
where in the world Is there in the world A

man so extra-or-di-naire?
man so un touch'd and pure?

[67] Allegretto scherzando

*(Spoken modestly) C'est moi...C'est moi! C'est moi, I'm forced to ad-mit! 'Tis
C'est moi! C'est moi, I blush to dis-close, I'm

I, I humbly re-ply. That mor-tal who These
far too no-ble to lie. That man in whom These

mar-vels can do, C'est moi, C'est moi, 'tis I! I've
qual-i-ties bloom, C'est moi, C'est moi, 'tis I! I've

*) 2nd stanza only

nev - er lost In bat - tle or game. I'm
nev - er stray'd From all I be - lieve. I'm

sim - ply the best by far. When
bless'd with an i - ron will. Had

swords are cross'd 'Tis al - ways the same, One
I been made The part - ner of Eve, We'd

blow and au re - voir! C'est
be in E - den still. C'est

moi! C'est moi, So admir-'bly fit; A
moi! C'est moi, The angels have chose To

French Prometheus unbound. ___ And here I stand with
fight their battles below. ___ And here I stand as

valor untold, Exception-'lly brave, amazingly bold, To
pure as a pray'r, Incredibly clean, with virtue to spare, The

serve at the Table Round! The
god-liest man I know! C'est moi!

*) Bars 97 and 98 are rit. in the 2nd stanza.

No. 11 — **The Lusty Month Of May**
(Dance And Song)

Cue: ARTHUR:... Welcome, Lancelot. Bless you for coming, and welcome to the table. *(The scene changes.)*

23
W.W., Hp.
Bells
Tpts.
W. Block
Str.
sfz
f
8va
f
+Tbn.
sub. mf
29
W.W., Hns., Str.
+Tbn.
37
+Tpts.

mf Tutti
45
W.W., Hns., Str.
f +Xyl.
mf
f Tbns.
f Tutti
mf
f
51
sfz
sfz
sfz
W.W. Br. Str.
Fl., Bsn., Mand.
mf

62

Cantabile
85
W.W.
Hns.
Str.
Hp.(gliss.)
f
Tutti
(Br.)
Hp.(gliss.)
cresc. sempre
91
ff
97
W.W.
Mand.
Vls.
sffz
mf
grazioso
Cl.
Hns.
103
Tpts.

Tpts.
Tpts., Xyl.
109
W.W., Hp.
Tutti
sfz
L'istesso tempo
mf marcato
Cl., Bsn., Hns.,
Tbs., Vc., Bs.
Vls.
tr
Timp.
8
115
+ W.W., Vls. 8va
+Tpt.
Timp.
8

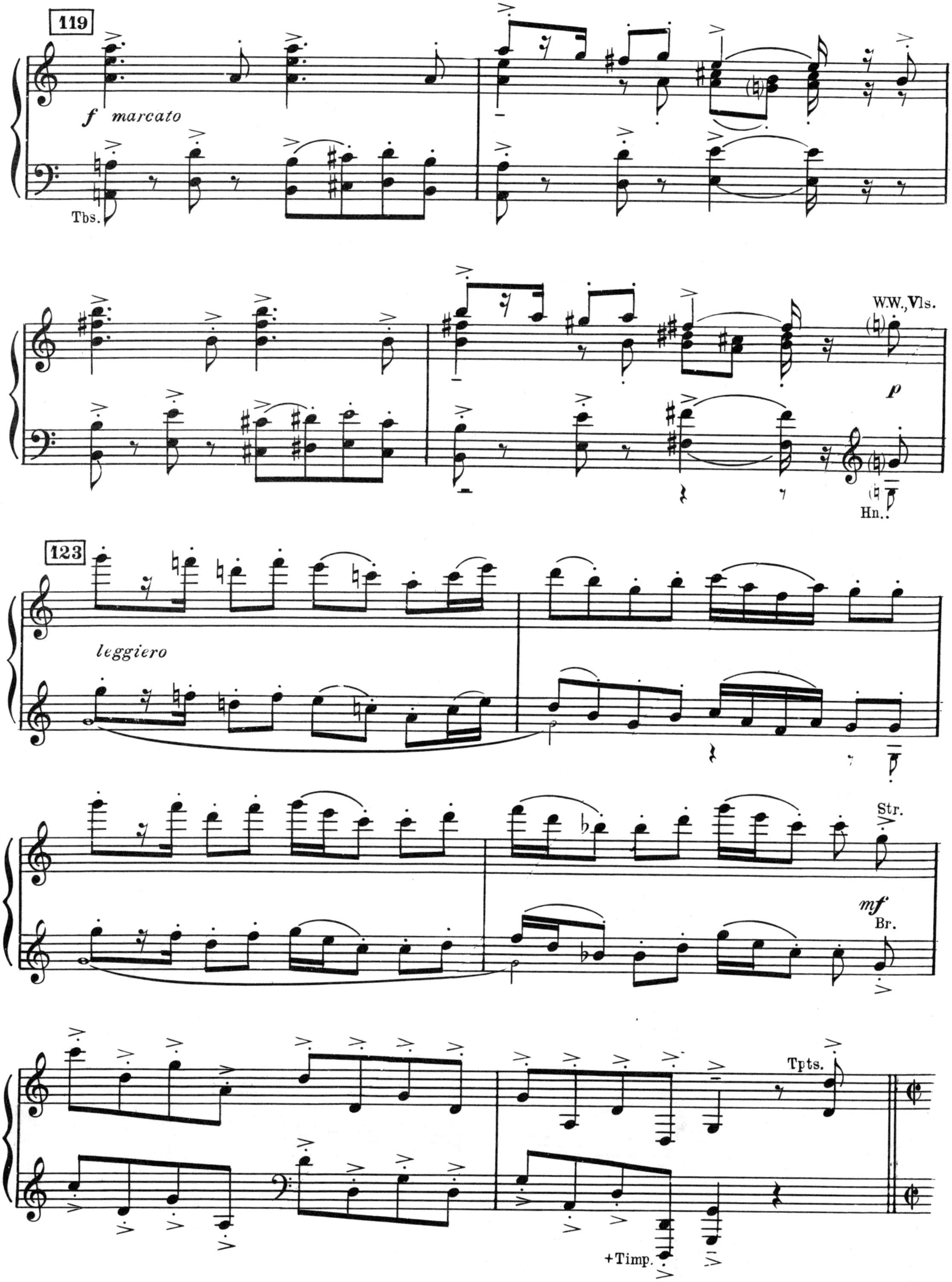
119
f marcato
Tbs.
W.W., Vls.
p
Hn.
123
leggiero
Str.
mf
Br.
Tpts.
+Timp.

W.W.
129
mf
Tutti
(Tbns.)
136
mf
subito
141
cresc. poco a poco
marc.
147
GUENEVERE:
Tra
allargando
ff

Allegretto giocoso

la! It's May! The lust-y month of May! That love-ly month when ev-'ry-one goes Bliss-ful-ly a-stray. Tra la! It's here! That shock-ing time of year! When tons of wick-ed lit-tle thoughts mer-ri-ly ap-pear. It's

May! It's May! That gor-geous hol-i-day; When ev-'ry maid-en prays that her lad Will be a cad! It's mad! It's gay! A li-bel-ous dis-play. Those drear-y vows that ev-'ry one takes, Ev-'ry-one breaks. Ev-'ry-one makes di-

vine mis-takes The lust-y month of May! Whence this fra-grance waft-ing through the air? What sweet feel-ings does its scent trans-mute? Whence this per-fume float-ing ev - 'ry — where? Don't you know it's that dear for-bid-den fruit!

CHORUS: Soprani *pp leggiere*
Alti
Tra la la

200

Tra la la la la. That dear for-bid-den fruit! Tra la la la la!

S. la ⸺

A. la ⸺

T. *pp leggiero* Tra la la la ⸺

B. *pp leggiero* Tra la la la ⸺

Tra la la la la mp Tra
mp Tra la la la la! Tra la la la la
mp Tra la la la la! mp Tra la la la la
mp Tra la la la la
mp Tra la la la la
+Hn
206
(♩ = ♩.)
la! Tra la! Tra la la la la la la la la
Tra la! Tra la!
Tra la! Tra la!
Tra la! Tra la! la
la
Bar.
Tra la! Tra la!
206 Fl. Ob. Tpt.
mf
Str.
Cls.
pp
etc.
Bsn., Hn.
S.Dr.
etc.

cresc. molto
212
la
It's
cresc. molto
la la la la la la la la la la la la la!
cresc. molto
la la la la la la la la la la!
cresc. molto
la la la la la la la!
cresc. molto
Bass
la la la la la la la la!
W.W.
212
Str.
cresc.
Hns.
f +Br.
p
GUENEVERE:
May! The lust - y month of May! That dar - ling month when
Cls.
etc.

ev-'ry-one throws Self-con-trol a-way. It's

S.A.: Tra la la

T.B.: Tra la la

220

time to do A wretch-ed thing or two, And

Lute

try to make each pre-cious day One you'll al-ways rue. It's

May! It's May! The month of "yes you may," The time for ev-'ry friv-o-lous whim, Prop-er or "im." It's

S. Tra la Tra la

A. Tra la Tra la

T. Tra la Tra la

236
a tempo
wild! It's gay! A blot in ev - 'ry way. The
S.
mp
Tra la Tra la Tra la la
A.
mp
Tra la Tra la Tra la la
T.
p
mp
la la la Tra la la
B.
p
mp
la la la Tra la la
236
W.W.
a tempo
birds and bees with all of their vast A-mor-ous past Gaze at the hu-man

245
race a - ghast The lust - y month
The lust - y month
The lust - y month
The lust - y month
The lust - y month
245
W.W.
+Hns.
+Tbn.
of May!
of May!
of May!
of May!
of May!
Tutti

GUENEVERE:
Tra la! It's May! The lust-y month of May!

Tra la la la Tra la la la la la la That
Tra la la la Tra la la la la la la That
Tra la la la Tra la la la la la la la la That
Tra la la la Tra la la la la la la That

Tra
ALL:
love - ly month when ev-'ry one goes_ Bliss - ful - ly a - stray. Tra
ALL:
la when ev-'ry one goes_ Bliss - ful - ly a - stray. Tra
la when ev-'ry one goes_ Bliss - ful - ly a - stray.
love - ly month when ev-'ry one goes_ Bliss - ful - ly a - stray.
Cls., Vls.
Br.
Bsn.
Hns.
Vc.
Bs.
263
la! It's here! That shock - ing time of year! When
la! It's here! That shock - ing time of year! When
la! It's here! That shock - ing time of year! Tra la la When
ALL:
Tra la! It's here! Tra la la When
ALL:
Tra la! It's here! When
263
W.W.
Bells
Str.
f Tutti

tons of wick-ed lit-tle thoughts mer-ri-ly ap-pear.
tons of wick-ed lit-tle thoughts mer-ri-ly ap-pear.
tons of wick-ed lit-tle thoughts mer-ri-ly ap-pear.
tons of wick-ed lit-tle thoughts mer-ri-ly ap-pear. It's
tons of wick-ed lit-tle thoughts mer-ri-ly ap-pear. It's

It's May! It's May! great dis-may; When
It's May! It's May! great dis-may;
May! It's May! The month of great dis-may;
May! It's May! The month of great dis-may;

all the world is brim-ming with fun, Whole-some or "un."

ALL: It's

ALL: It's

S. Tra-la! Tra-la! la la la Tra la la! These
A. mad! It's gay! A li-bel-ous dis-play; Tra la la! These
T. Tra la! Tra la! A li-bel-ous dis-play; Tra la la! These
B. mad! It's gay! A li-bel-ous dis-play; Tra la la! These

cresc. al fine
drear - y vows that ev - 'ry-one takes, Ev - 'ry-one breaks. Ev - 'ry-one makes di -
drear - y vows that Ev - 'ry-one breaks. Ev - 'ry-one makes di -
drear - y vows that Ev - 'ry-one breaks. Ev - 'ry-one makes di -
drear - y vows that ev - 'ry - one takes, Ev - 'ry-one breaks. Ev - 'ry-one makes di -
Tbns.
288
vine mis - takes The lust - y month of May!
vine mis - takes The lust - y month of May!
vine mis - takes The lust - y month of May!
vine mis - takes The lust - y month of May!
f
Tpts.
Hns.
ff

82

Segue

No. 11a

Pellinore's Entrance

No. 12 End Of Scene

Cue: SIR LIONEL: He shall have my challenge in the morning.
    GUENEVERE: Thank you, Sir Lionel.
    SIR SAGRAMORE: And mine.
    GUENEVERE: Thank you, Sir Sagramore.
    SIR DINADAN: And mine.

Allegretto giocoso

GUENEVERE: Tra la! It's May! The lusty month of May! That darling month when ev'ry-one throws Self-control a-way.

CHORUS: (*unisono*) It's mad! It's gay! A libelous display: Those

84

85

No. 13 Change Of Scene

No. 14 How To Handle A Woman

Cue: GUENEVERE: ...let him command me! And Yours Humbly will graciously obey. What? What? *(She exits)*
ARTHUR: What?
Blast!
Blast you, Merlyn!
This is all your fault!

(Vivace) ARTHUR: *(He sings)*

You swore that you had taught me ev-'ry-thing from A to Zed, With nar-y an o-mis-sion in be-tween. Well, I shall tell you what You ob-vious-ly for-got: That's how a rul-er rules a Queen!

And what of teach-ing me by turn-ing me to an-i-mal and bird, From beav-er to the small-est bob-o-link! I should have had a whirl At chang-ing to a girl, To learn the way the crea-tures think!

[45] Tranquillo
was-n't there a night, on a sum-mer long gone by, We pass'd a cou-ple wran-gling a-

[49]
way;— And did I not say, Mer-lyn: What if that chap were I? And

90

did he not give coun-sel and say... What was it now? My mind's a wall. Oh, yes! By jove, now I re-call:

57 Moderato

How to han-dle a wom-an? There's a way, said the wise old man; A way known by ev-'ry wom-an Since the whole rig-'ma-role be-gan. Do I flat-ter her? I begged him

an-swer. Do I threat-en or ca-jole or plead? Do I

brood or play the gay ro-manc-er? Said he, smil-ing: No in-

deed. How to han-dle a wom-an? Mark me

well, I will tell you, Sir: The way to handle a woman Is to love her... simply love her... Merely love her... love her... love her. He

[87] *ponders a moment, then says:* What's wrong, Jenny? Where are you these days? What are you thinking? I don't understand you. But no matter. Merlyn told me once: Never be too [95] disturbed if you don't understand what a woman is thinking. They don't do it often. But what do you do when they are doing it? *(He sings)* [103] How to han-dle a wom-an? Mark me

well, I will tell you, Sir: The way to handle a woman Is to love her... simply love her ____ Merely love her... love her ____ love her.

(Curtain)

attacca

No. 15 — Tent Scene

The curtain rises. SIR LIONEL, SIR DINADAN, SIR SAGRAMORE with their squires, and
W.W., Vls.
etc.
sempre f
Br.
+Bells
LANCELOT with DAP are preparing for the joust.
27
gliss.
Hp.
31
W.W.,
Bells,
Str.
Bsn., Tbns.
Tpts.
ff
Dr.
(Dialogue)
LANCELOT: I wish you success, Milords.
(Dialogue continues)

No. 16 — The Tumblers

Cue: SIR DINADAN: ... How benevolent. Do you know what I shall be thinking, Lancelot, when I see you on your horse? There he is, the Sermon on the mount.

98

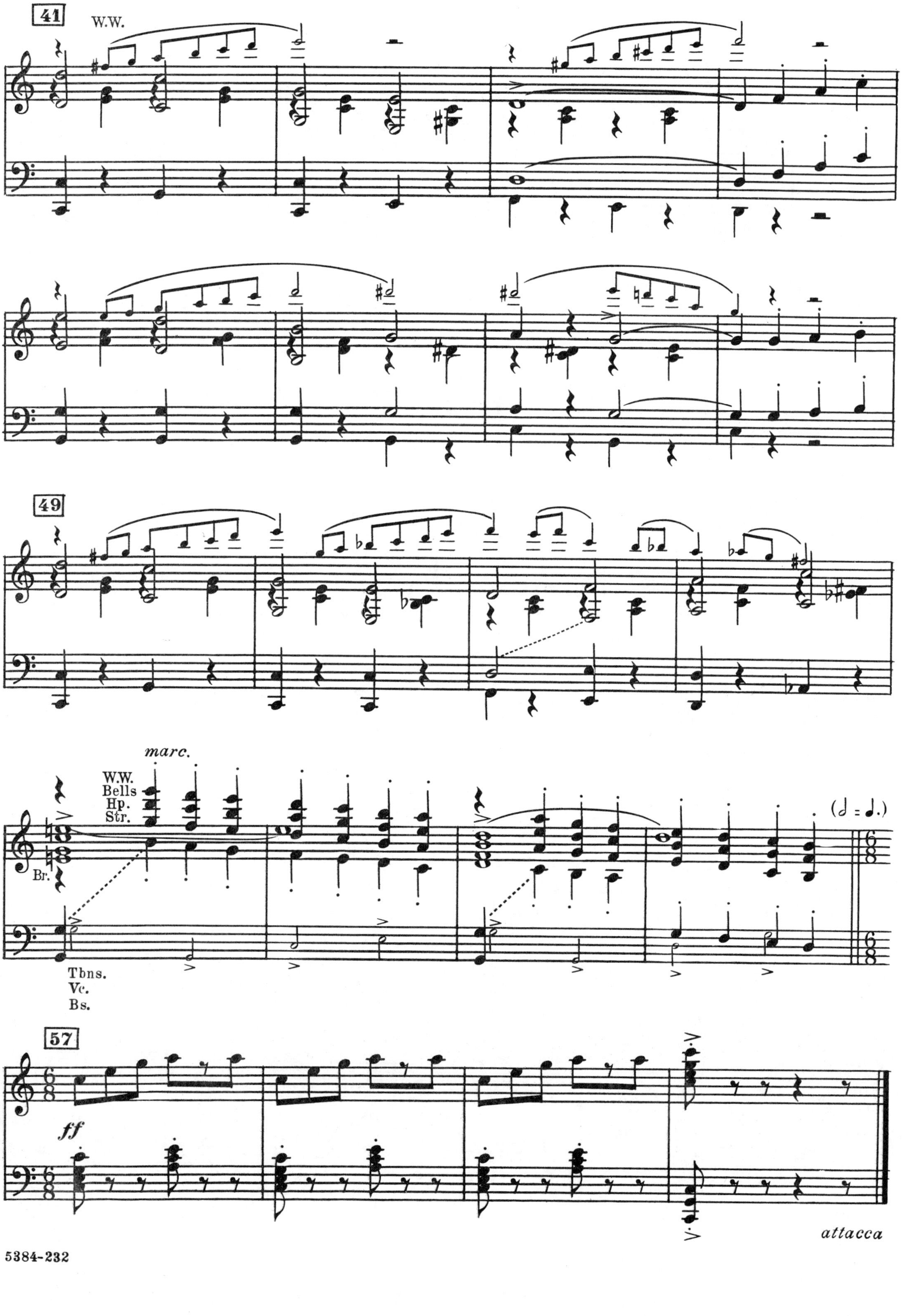
41
W.W.
49
marc.
W.W.
Bells
Hp.
Str.
Br.
Tbns.
Vc.
Bs.
57
ff
attacca

No. 17 The Jousts

Alla marcia

MAN: *(shouted)* Sir Dinadan's in form and feeling in his prime.

GROUP: *(sung)* Yah! Yah! Yah! Oh, we'll all have a glorious time!

ANOTHER MAN: *(shouted)* Sir Sagramore is fit, and Sir Li-'nel feels sublime.

ALL: *(sung)* Yah! Yah! Yah! Oh, we'll

Copyright © 1960 (unpub.) & 1962 by Alan Jay Lerner and Frederick Loewe

19
ALL MEN:
all have a glo - ri - ous time! Now look you there! Sir
sfz mf
Tutti
Hns.
ALL WOMEN:
(spoken)
He's a - stride! Oh look!
Din - a - dan's a - stride. It's ob - vious he will
27
ALL: (shouting)
Good for - tune, Din - a - dan! We
ALL: (shouting)
be the first to ride. Good for - tune, Din - a - dan! We
W.W., Vls.
W.W., Tpts.

102

ALL WOMEN:
39
mf
Sir Din-a-dan! Sir Din-a-dan! Oh, there he goes with
ALL MEN: mf
Sir Din-a-dan! Sir Din-a-dan! Oh, there he goes with
Vls.
Bsn. Hns. Vla. Vc.
pp
all his might and main.
MAN:
There he goes!
(ALL:)
He's got a stead-y
all his might and main.
He's got a stead-y
E♭ Cl.
Picc.
pp
+Hp. Dr., Bs.
WOMAN: (shouting) Stead-y! Stead-y! Stead-y!
grip up-on his rein.
grip up-on his rein.
+W.W. 3rd Tpt.
fp
fp

51
(ALL:)
Stead-y! Sir Din-a-dan! Sir Din-a-dan! Oh, try to gal-lop
Stead-y! Sir Din-a-dan! Sir Din-a-dan! Oh, try to gal-lop
Vls.
Bsn. Hns. Vla. Vc.
WOMAN: (shouting)
On the right! On the right!
by him on the right. For that's the arm where
by him on the right. For that's the arm where
E♭ Cl.
Picc.
+Hp. Dr., Bs.
(shouting)
you have all the might. MAN:
On the right!
On the right, On the
(ALL:) (shouting)
you have all the might. On the right, On the
+W.W. 3rd Tpt.
Tbns.

105

106

blow! Here comes the blow! Oh, NO!

MAN: (spoken) *p*
'Twas luck, that's all it was; pure luck and nothing more.

WOMAN: (spoken)
Sagramore will even up the score.

ANOTHER MAN: *mf* (spoken)
The Frenchman struck him first, but the blow was not that great.

5384-232

ANOTHER WOMAN: (spoken) Sa-gra-more, will o-pen up his pate.

ALL WOMEN: (sung) Sir

SOME MEN: (sung) Sir

[101] Sa-gra-more! He's rid-ing on the field!

Sa-gra-more! He's rid-ing on the field!

ANOTHER MAN: (spoken) Oh, there's the black and crim-son of his shield.

ALL: (sung) There he

ALL: (sung) There he

108

109 Allegro agitato

goes! There he goes! He's bending low and spurring on his
goes! There he goes! He's bending low and spurring on his

steed.
WOMAN: There he goes!
ALL: (sung) He's charging him with
steed. He's charging him with

record breaking speed.
WOMAN: (shouting) Charge! Charge!
ALL: (sung) Sa-gra-
record breaking speed. Sa-gra-

more! Oh, make his ar-mor crack and split in two.

ANOTHER WOMAN: *(screaming)* Crack him! ALL: *(sung)* A might-y whack as on-ly you can do. ANOTHER WOMAN: Whack him! ALL: *(sung)* Now

133
cresc.
look you through the dust, LL - - - Look! Sir
look you through the dust, LL - - - Look! Sir
Bsn., Tbns.
Timp., Hp.
Sa - gra - more is read - y for the thrust, And
Sa - gra - more is read - y for the thrust, And
WOMAN: Split him!
ALL:
now they're cir - cling round. Sir
now they're cir - cling round. Sir

Sa-gra-more will drive him to the ground! Here comes the blow! Here comes the blow! Oh, NO!

ARTHUR: *(In the grandstand)* He did that rath-er well, don't you think, dear?

GUENEVERE: That horse of Sa-gra-more's is too old. But

Sir Din-a-dan, I'm told, has a nast-y fell-ing Din-a-dan with one blow, dear. cold.

163 Allegro agitato

S: Sir Li-o-nel! Sir Li-o-nel! Oh, charge at him and
A: Sir Li-o-nel! Sir Li-o-nel! Oh, charge at him and
T: Sir Li-o-nel! Sir Li-o-nel! Oh, charge him!
Oh, charge at him and
B: Sir Li-o-nel! Sir Li-o-nel! Oh, charge him!

throw him off his horse! Go! Oh, show him what we
throw him off his horse! Go! Oh, show him what we
Oh, show him!
throw him off his horse! Go! Oh, show him what we
Go! Oh, show him!

WOMAN: Throw him down! *(shouted)*

mean by Eng-lish force!
mean by Eng-lish force!
mean by Eng-lish force!

175
ALL:
mf (sung)
Down! Sir Li-o-nel! Sir Li-o-nel! I've nev-er seen him
ALL:
mf (sung)
Down! Sir Li-o-nel! Sir Li-o-nel! I've nev-er seen him
ALL:
(optional)
Down! Sir Li-o-nel! Sir Li-o-nel! I've nev - er!
I've nev-er seen him
ALL:
mf (sung)
Down! Sir Li-o-nel! Sir Li-o-nel! I've nev - er!
175
W.W.
pp
Str.
(colle voci)
Ob.
Bsn.
ev-er ride as fast. Yah! That French-man will be
f (sung)
ev-er ride as fast. Yah! That French-man will be
f (sung)
(sung)
That French - man!
ev-er ride as fast. Yah! That French-man will be
f (sung)
Yah! That French - man!
Tutti
ff
Hns., Str.

hope-less-ly out-class'd. Yah! Yah! Yah! Yah!

Yah! His spear is in the air! I

116

tell you Lance-lot has-n't got a pray'r, His shield is much too
tell you Lance-lot has-n't got a pray'r, His shield is much too
tell you Lance-lot has-n't got a pray'r, His shield is much too
tell you Lance-lot has-n't got a pray'r, His shield is much too

199

WOMAN: *(shouting)* Charge! *(sung)*

low. A good hard thrust and down-ward he will
low. A good hard thrust and down-ward he will
low. A good hard thrust and down-ward he will
low. A good hard thrust and down-ward he will

W.W.

Hp.

5384-232

go! And here's the blow! Here comes the
blow! Oh, NO! Oh, NO!

Sir Lionel is down! Dear God it isn't true! Sir Lionel is dead! The spear has run him through!

219
SIR LIONEL is carried on... ARTHUR descends from the grandstand...pulls a blanket over his face.
Adagio (♩ = 80)
lunga
fff Tutti
dim.
poco a
f poco
mf (Str.)
p
pp
morendo
lunga
LANCELOT enters, kneels beside SIR LIONEL and prays. Slowly, SIR LIONEL moves - the crowd gasps.
lunga
lunga
227
Andante sostenuto
LANCELOT rises,
W.W.
Hn.
Str.
p legato
235
slowly walks away, stops before GUENEVERE, and bows humbly.
Hn.
cresc.
As he rises, she looks at him and curtsies before him.
247
(+3Hns.)
f dim. molto
pp
cresc. poco
Timp.
Their eyes are transfixed on each other.
(Tpts.)
a poco
Tutti
ff
(Curtain)
attacca

No. 18
Change Of Scene

No.19 **Before I Gaze At You Again** 121

Cue: ARTHUR: It might do you good to get away from Round Tables and chivalry for a little while. Don't you think?
(GUENEVERE *does not answer*)
Don't you think? (*She still doesn't answer. He turns and exits.*)
GUENEVERE: Oh, Lance, go away...

(She continues)... Go away and don't come back.

(She sings) Be-fore I gaze at you a-gain I'll need a time for tears. Be-fore I gaze at you a-gain Let

5384-232 Copyright © 1960 (unpub.) & 1962 by Alan Jay Lerner and Frederick Loewe

hours turn to years. I have so much for-get-ting to do Be-fore I try to gaze a-gain at you.

[25] Poco più mosso

Stay a-way un-til you cross my mind

Bare-ly once a day; Till the mo-ment I a-wake and find I can smile and say: That I can gaze at you a-gain With-out a blush or qualm, My eyes a-shine like new a-gain, My

41
man-ner poised and calm. Stay far a-way, My
+Fl.
Br.
W.W.,Str.
mf
E.H.
pp
love, far a-way. Till I for-get I gazed at you to-
Str.
47
day. To-day To-
+W.W.
Vc. Solo
espr.
+E.H.
day.
Vl. Solo
(Dialogue)
(Vc. Solo)
p
mf
Hns.
Tbs.
Timp.
Segue

No. 20 — # Finale Act I — 125

Cue: ARTHUR: ... all borders will disappear ... and all the things I dreamed ... I dreamed ... I dreamed. *(Curtain)*
The scene changes to a corridor in the Castle.

Knights parade to the Great Hall with banners in a ceremonial drill.

126

The curtain rises on the Great Hall. Ladies and Gentlemen of
49
Con moto, moderato
W.W., Hns., Str.
Gtr.
Hp.
mf
the Court are filing in.
57
Ob.
p Hp., Bsn.
W.W., Hns., Str.
Gtr.
Hp.
poco rit.
ARTHUR and GUENEVERE enter and take their places on the throne!
65
Maestoso
(Tpts)
ff Tutti
sim.

ARTHUR: Excalibur!
Tpts.
Tbns.
ff Hns
Timp.
75
Andante con moto
SIR DINADAN: To be invested Knights of the Round Table of England: of Brackley... Colgrevance.
(Colgrevance steps forward
(Ob.)
mf
W.W.
pp
mf
83
and is knighted.) Of Winchester... Bliant.
(Bliant steps forward and is knighted.) Of Wales... Guilliam.
pp
mf
pp
Hn.
Hn.
(Guilliam steps forward and is knighted.) Of Cornwall...Castor.(Castor steps forward and is knighted.)
Of Joyous Gard: Lancelot Du Lac.
91
mf
Hns.
Hp.
pp
(Lancelot steps forward. ARTHUR hesitates, then he knights Lancelot.)
+Tpts.
mf
Hn.
cresc. e rit.
cresc. molto
+Tbn.
Hn.
Timp.

Moderato, solenne
100
W.W., Hns., Str.
Lute, Hp.
The Court slowly withdraws from the Great Hall. Everybody bows before ARTHUR.
f cantando
+ Tpts.
Hn., Vls.
ff
+Br.
108
(W.W., Vls.)
Tutti
W.W., Hns.
f sempre
Tpt.
Tbn.
Str.
Tutti
Hns.

ARTHUR: *(alone in the Great Hall)* Proposition: If I could choose, from every

woman who breathes on this earth, the face I would most love, the smile, the touch, the voice, the heart, the laugh, the soul itself, every detail and feature to the smallest strand of hair - they would all be Jenny's.

141 Proposition: If I could choose, from every man who breathes on this earth, a man for my brother

and a man for my son, a man for my friend, they would all be Lance.

149 Yes, I love them. I love them, and they answer me again with pain and torment. Be it sin or not sin, they betray

me in their hearts, and that's far sin enough. I see it in their eyes and feel it when they speak, and they must pay for it and be punished. I shan't be wounded and not return it in kind. I'm done with feeble hoping. I demand a man's vengeance.

161 Poco più grave

Proposition: I'm a King, not a man. And a civilized King. Could it possibly be civilized to destroy what I love? Could it possibly be civilized to love myself above all?

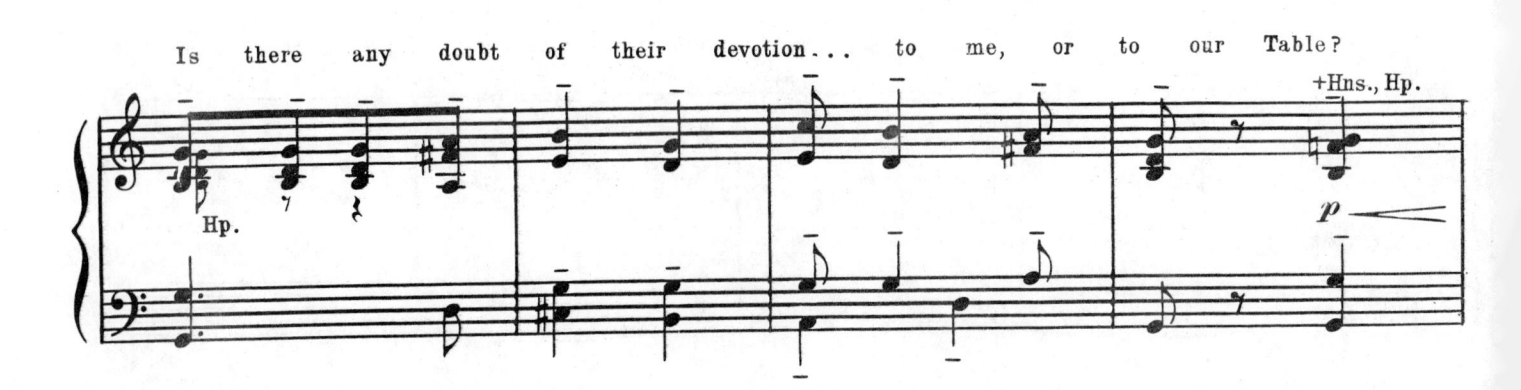

169 What of their pain and their torment? Did they ask for this calamity? Can passion be selected?

Is there any doubt of their devotion... to me, or to our Table?

177 By God, Excalibur, I shall be a King! This is the time of King Arthur, and we reach for the stars! This is the time of King Arthur, and

185 violence is not strength and compassion is not weakness. We are civilized! Resolved:

Ben tenuto

We shall live through this together, Excalibur... they... you... and I... And God have mercy on us all.

They're waiting for us at the Table. Let's not delay the celebration.

Largo, maestoso

(Curtain)

End of Act I

Entr'acte

No. 21

Allegro brillante

9
3
Hns.
+Vls.,Vlas.
(tr)
Tpts.
Tutti
dim.
16
Allegro moderato
pp
Str.
W.W.,Hns.
cresc.
Br.
Vls. 8va
f

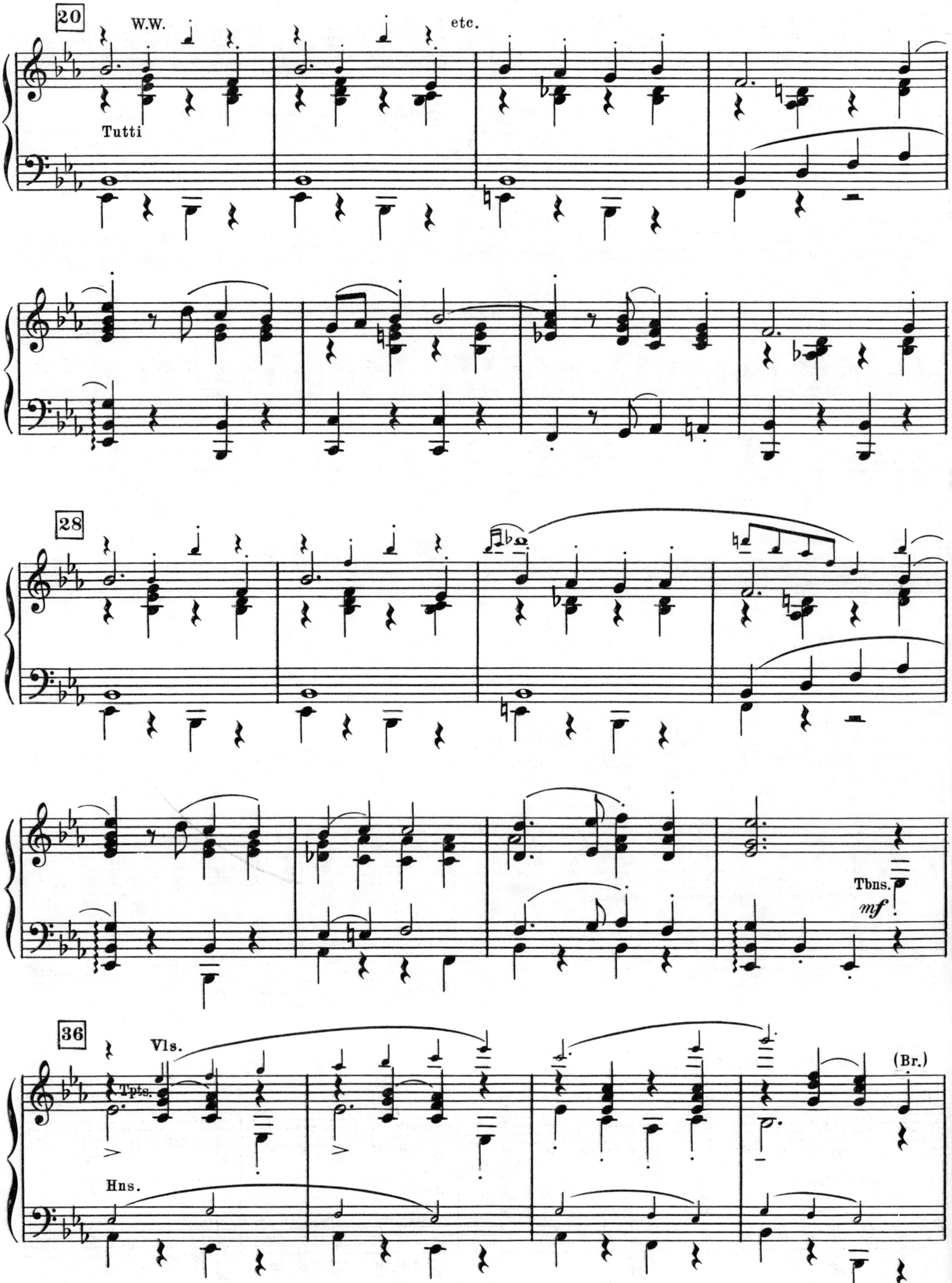
20
W.W.
etc.
Tutti
28
Tbns.
mf
36
Vls.
Tpts.
(Br.)
Hns.

137

60
Moderato
E.H., Bsn.
Hns., Str.
f
espr.
Tbns.
+W.W.
Tpts.
E.H.
Bsn.
Str.
Hp.
mf
68
Hns.
f Tutti
+Bells
poco rit.
76
E.H.
Bsn.
Hns.
Str.
mf
a tempo
Tbns.
+W.W.
Tpts.

82
(Tpt.I)
Fl., Cl.
Tbn.
p
+E.H.
Cl.II
(♩ = 𝅗𝅥)
rit.
W.W.
Allegro risoluto
Hns.
Br.
fp
Tpt.II
fp
Tpt.I
fp
W.W.
Xyl.
Vls.
f
92
Alla marcia
Tpts.
Tbns.
Tpts., Tbns.
W.W.
W.W.
sf
Tutti

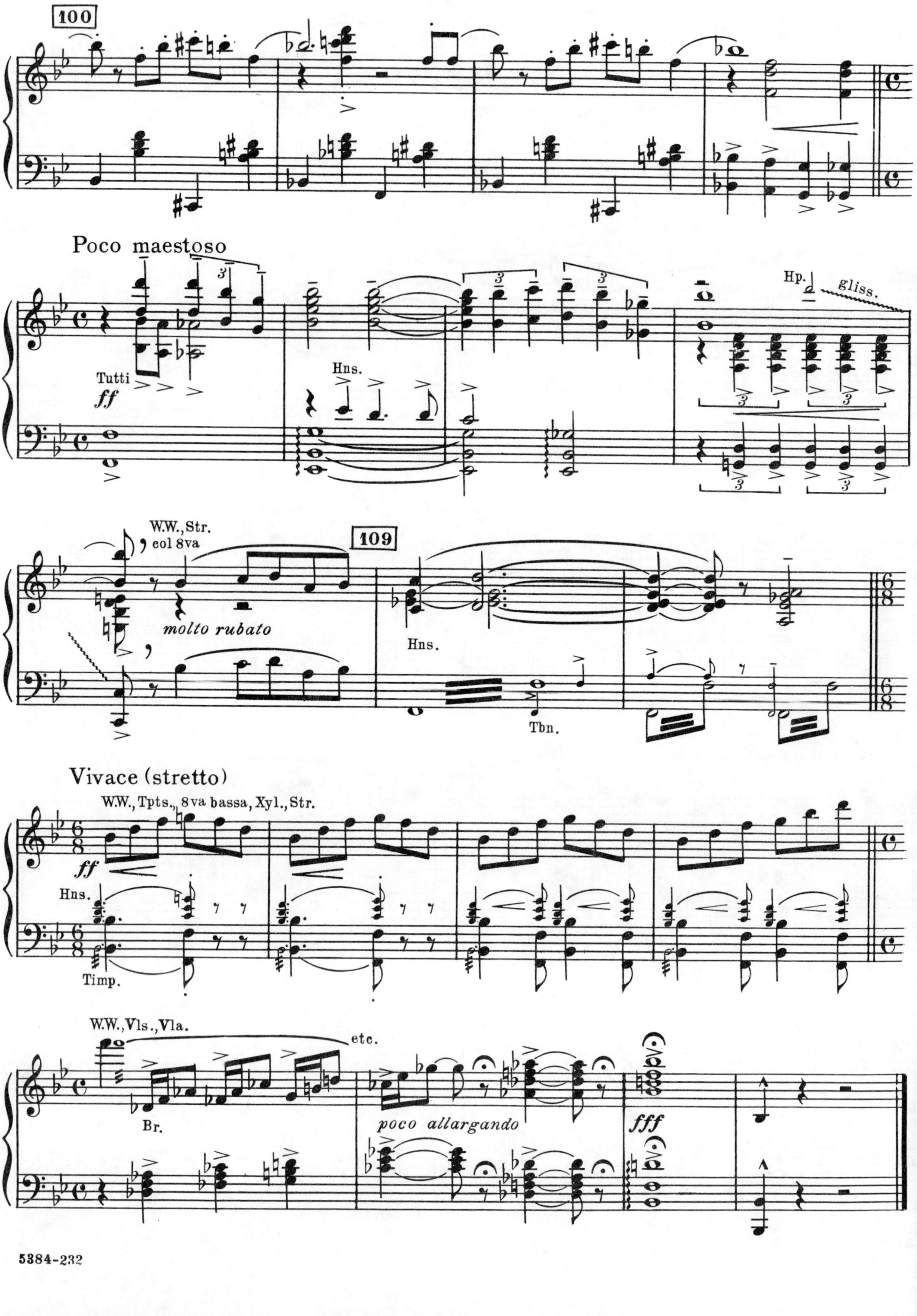
100
Poco maestoso
Tutti
ff
Hns.
Hp.
gliss.
W.W., Str.
col 8va
109
molto rubato
Hns.
Tbn.
Vivace (stretto)
W.W., Tpts., 8va bassa, Xyl., Str.
ff
Hns.
Timp.
W.W., Vls., Vla.
etc.
Br.
poco allargando
fff

No. 22
Madrigal And "If Ever I Would Leave You"

142

25 Moderato LANCELOT: *(Sings a madrigal to GUENEVERE.)*

Tou - jours j'ai eu le mê - me voeux, Sur terre une dé - es - se, au ciel un Dieu. Un hom-me dé-sire pour êt - re heu-reux Sur terre une dé - es - se, au ciel un Dieu. Years may come; years may go; This, I know, will e'er be so: The reason to live is only to love A goddess on earth and a God above.

GUENEVERE: Did you write that, Lance?

LANCELOT: GUENEVERE: LANCELOT:
Yes. Why do you always write about you? I can't write about you.
Why don't you ever write about me? I love you too much. Jenny, I should leave you,

and never come back. I've said it to myself day after day, year after year. But how can I? Look at you. When

If Ever I Would Leave You

Con espressione
(He sings)

would I?

If ev-er I would leave you   It would-n't be in

Copyright © 1960 by Alan Jay Lerner and Frederick Loewe

sum-mer;___ See-ing you in sum-mer, I nev-er would go.___ Your hair streaked with sun-light...___ Your lips red as flame...___ Your face with a lus-tre___ That puts gold to shame.___ But if I'd ev-er leave you,___ It could-n't be in

au-tumn. How I'd leave in au-tumn, I nev-er would know. I've seen how you spar-kle When fall nips the air. I know you in au-tumn And I must be there. And could I leave you run-ning mer-ri-ly through the snow? Or on a win-try eve-ning when you catch the fi-re's glow? If ev-er I would leave you, How could it be in spring-time, Know-ing how in spring I'm be-witch'd by you so? Oh, no, not in spring-time! Sum-mer, win-ter or

fall! No, nev-er could I leave you at all. *passionato* If ev-er I would leave you, How could it be in

spring-time, Knowing how in spring I'm be-witch'd by you so? Oh, no, not in spring-time! Sum-mer, win-ter or fall! No, nev-er could I leave you at all.

No. 23 **The Seven Deadly Virtues** 149

Cue: ARTHUR: The adage "blood is thicker than water", was invented by undeserving relatives. *(He exits)*
MORDRED: Virtue and proper deeds, Your Majesty, like what?

Courage, Milord? Purity and humility, my liege? Diligence? Charity? Honesty? Fidelity?

The seven deadly virtues? No, thank you, Your Majesty. *(He sings)* **7** Vivo

The sev-en dead-ly vir-tues, Those ghast-ly lit-tle traps, Oh, no, Mi-lord, they were-n't meant for me. Those sev-en dead-ly vir-tues, They're made for oth-er

5384-232 Copyright © 1960 (unpub.) & 1962 by Alan Jay Lerner and Frederick Loewe

chaps, Who love a life of fail-ure and en-nui. Take

23 Cour-age! Now there's a sport... An in-vi-ta-tion to the

31 state of rig-or mort! And Pur-i-ty! A no-ble

yen! And ver-y rest-ful ev-'ry now and then.

39
I find Hu-mil-i-ty means to be hurt; It's not the
p
Hns.
f
earth the meek in-her-it, it's the dirt.
+Br.
W.W.
Bells, Hp.
47
Hon-es-ty is
Hns.
fa-tal and should be ta-boo. Dil-i-gence? A fate I would
55
hate. If Char-i-ty means giv-ing, I give it to
W.W.
Tpts.

you, And Fi-del-i-ty is on-ly for your mate. You'll nev-er find a vir-tue Un-sta-tus-ing my quo, Or mak-ing my Be-el-za-bub-ble burst. Let oth-ers take the high road, I will take the low; I cannot wait to rush in Where angels fear to go. With all those seven deadly virtues, Free and happy little me has not been cursed.

(Curtain) attacca

No. 24 Change Of Scene

No. 25 **What Do The Simple Folk Do?**

155

Cue: GUENEVERE: Royalty never can. Why is that, Arthur? Other people do. They seem to have ways and means of finding respite. What do they do? Farmers, cooks, blacksmiths.....

Moderato

GUENEVERE: What do the sim-ple folk do ___ To help them es-cape when they're blue? ___ The shep-herd who is ail-ing, The milk-maid who is glum, The cob-bler who is wail-ing From nail-ing His thumb?

5384-232 Copyright © 1960 (unpub.) & 1961 by Alan Jay Lerner and Frederick Loewe

When they're be-set and be-sieged, The folk not no-bless'-ly o-bliged... How-ev-er do they man-age To shed their wea-ry lot? Oh, what do sim-ple folk do _____ We do not? _____

ARTHUR: (*seriously*)
I have been in-formed By those who know them well, They find re-lief in quite a clev-er way. _____ When they're sore-ly pressed, They whis-tle for a spell; And

158

whis-tling seems to bright-en up their day. _____ And that's _____ what sim-ple folk do; _____ So they say. _____

GUENEVERE: *(spoken)*
They whistle?

ARTHUR:
So they say. _____

65
(GUENEVERE begins to whistle.)
Cls.
p
Str., pizz., Hp.
(ARTHUR joins in)
73
Gtr., Str. arco
(GUENEVERE suddenly stops, thinks for a moment, then turns to him.)
GUENEVERE:
What
dim.
pp

160

else do the simple folk do _____ To perk up the heart and get through? _____ The wee folk and the grown folk Who wander to and fro Have ways known to their own folk We throne folk Don't know.

When all the doldrums begin, What keeps each of them in his skin? What ancient native custom Provides the needed glow? Oh, what do simple folk

113

do?_____ Do you know?_____

ARTHUR:
Once a-long the road I came up-on a lad

121
Sing-ing in a voice three times his size._____

When I asked him why, He told me he was sad, And

singing always made his spirits rise. So that's what simple folk do, I surmise.

GUENEVERE: *(spoken)* They sing?
ARTHUR: I surmise.
BOTH: A-

rise, my love! A-rise my love! A-pol-lo's light-ing the skies, my love. The mead-ows shine With col-um-bine And daf-fo-dils blos-som a-way. Hear Ve-nus call To one and all: Come taste de-light while you may.

ARTHUR: The world is bright, And

(GUENEVERE turns to him in frustration.)

GUENEVERE: all is right, And life is merry and gay! — What else do the simple folk do? — They must have a system or two. — They obviously outshine us At turning tears to mirth; Have tricks a roy-al high-ness Is min-us From birth.

177 What then, I won-der do they To

chase all the gob-lins a-way? They

185 have some tri-bal sorc'-ry You have-n't men-tioned yet. Oh, what do sim-ple folk do To for-get?

ARTHUR: Of-ten I am told They dance a fier-y dance, And whirl til they're com-plete-ly un-con-trolled.

Soon the mind is blank, And all are in a trance, A vi'lent trance astounding to behold. And that's what simple folk do, So I'm told.

(ARTHUR invites GUENEVERE to dance.)

Bsn., Hns.

f Tutti

(They dance a wild hornpipe.)

225 Poco più mosso

233

f sempre

(GUENEVERE sits hopelessly in her chair.)

GUENEVERE: What else do the simple folk do to help them escape when they're blue?

ARTHUR: They

265
sit a-round and won-der What roy-al folk would do, And that's
Bells
Str., W.W.
+Hns.
GUENEVERE: (spoken) Really?
what sim - ple folk do.
Vls.
Str.
pp espr.
rit.
Bsn.
ARTHUR: I have it on the best authority.
BOTH:
273 Poco meno mosso
Yes, that's what sim - ple
+W.W.
Cls.
Str.
Tempo Io
(Curtain)
folk do.
ff
Tutti
Hp.
sffz
attacca

No. 26 The Enchanted Forest

Allegro *(Change of scene)*

9 MORDRED *enters.*

MORDRED: Morgan Le Fey?... Morgan Le Fey?... Sister of my Mother, it's I, Mordred, who comes to visit you. Am I near your invisible castle?... Am I, dear Morgan?... dear sweet Aunt Morgan?... dear sweet Queen Aunt Morgan? Can you not hear me?

MORGAN LE FEY: *(from a distance)* Go away, Mordred. Go away! You were a nasty little boy, and I'm told you've become a nastier little man.

25 Andante

MORDRED: I beseech you,

Your Majesty, give me a moment of your time.
MORGAN: Not now, Mordred, I am eating my dinner and shan't be finished till tomorrow.
MORDRED: What a pity, I have chocolates.
Cymb.
Ped.
31
MORGAN: Chocolates? You say you have chocolates?
MORDRED: Hard candies and caramels!
MORGAN: Hard candies and caramels?
W.W., Hp.
MORDRED: Cherry creams with soft centers!
MORGAN: Cherry creams with soft centers?
Don't move, my darling nephew! Your darling aunt is on her way. Court!
Hp., Bell
Str.
ff in tempo
p cresc.
Hns. cresc. molto
Timp.
gliss.
Hp.
Tempo di Polka
37
The curtain rises on the Enchanted Forest.
f Tutti
41
Gaily
Weird and startling members of Queen Morgan's Court appear.
(Tpt.)
ff Tutti
(Br.)
Hns.

49
(Tpt.I)
Tutti
(Br.)
Hns.
W.W.
f sempre
Br., Str.
57
W.W., Vls.
Hns.
Tbns.
Hns.
Tbns.

65
W.W., Vls.
+Xyl.
Tbns.
Hns.
Tutti
Hp.
gliss.
ff
73
Tpts.
f sempre
Hns.
Tbns.
etc.
W.W.
Vlns.
Hns., Tbns.
81
W.W., Str., Xyl.
ff Hns.

176

114
W.W., Vls.
etc.
sfz
Tpts.
più f
Hns.
Tbns.
121
Tutti
Xyl.
gliss.
ff
(Tutti)
sffz
(Dialogue)
Hns., Tbns.

No. 27 — The Persuasion

Cue: MORGAN LE FEY: How do you know I build invisible walls?
    MORDRED: Mummy told me. Please, dear aunt?
    MORGAN: No, I will not harm little Wart. Court!

Farewell, nasty Mordred!

Waltz tempo

MORDRED: *(spoken rhythmically)*

E-nough can-dy I'll bring To fur-nish a new wing. Mass-es and mass-es Of gum-my mo-las-ses. Fudge by the van!

25
Fresh mar - zi - pan!
+Tpt.
mf
Bsn.
Vc.
All yours it will be If you
p Hn.
33
build me a wee Lit - tle wall.
+Br.
p
37
Xyl.
etc. MORGAN:
Do you
mf Tutti

45
prom - ise, you dev - il, It's all on the lev - el?
Tbn. I
Tbn. II
mf Tutti
MORDRED:
I sol - emn - ly swear It's a
p
53
MORGAN:
harm - less af - fair. On your hon - or, dear
mf Tutti
W.W. Str.
p
MORDRED:
lad? Hon - or? You're mad!
mf Tutti
p
W.W. Str.

181

MORGAN: Ye Gods, but you're low! My answer is "NO" And that's all!

MORDRED: A basket or two Of marsh-mel-low goo!

A lic-o-rice stick That takes two years to lick!

MORGAN: Where's the King? Bring the King! I'll build him a wall Three and sev-en feet tall! I'll hur-ry and mix Some in-vis-i-ble bricks.

MORDRED: Oh, Queen, you're a joy!

MORGAN: Be-gone, nasty boy!

MORDRED leaves.

MORGAN hides behind a tree.

KING ARTHUR and PELLINORE enter.

Allegro

Where's the bird? You hit it. I saw it. Where did it go?

PELLINORE: Where's the bird, Arthur?

ARTHUR: Strange, Pelly, I've never seen this forest before. I used to play in this valley, when I was a boy. But it was like a meadow. There were no trees.
PELLINORE: Nature, old boy. Things pop up, you know. Where's the bird?

ARTHUR: Sh-h-h. It's awfully quiet around here, isn't it? *(MORGAN appears and listens)* Not a leaf rustling, not a whisper in the woods..... It makes one feel rather drowsy. Would you care to rest a bit?

PELLINORE: No thank you, old man. I want to find that bird, what? I mean, if you hit a bird with an arrow, it ought to fall down like a gentleman. *(He exits)*

ARTHUR: Merlyn, do you remember how often we walked this valley when I was a boy? Do you know what I miss of those days? Not my youth. My innocence. My innocence. *(He closes his eyes)*

No. 28   The Invisible Wall

Morgan Le Fey's Court appears, carrying imaginary bricks. She directs the building of a wall around Arthur.

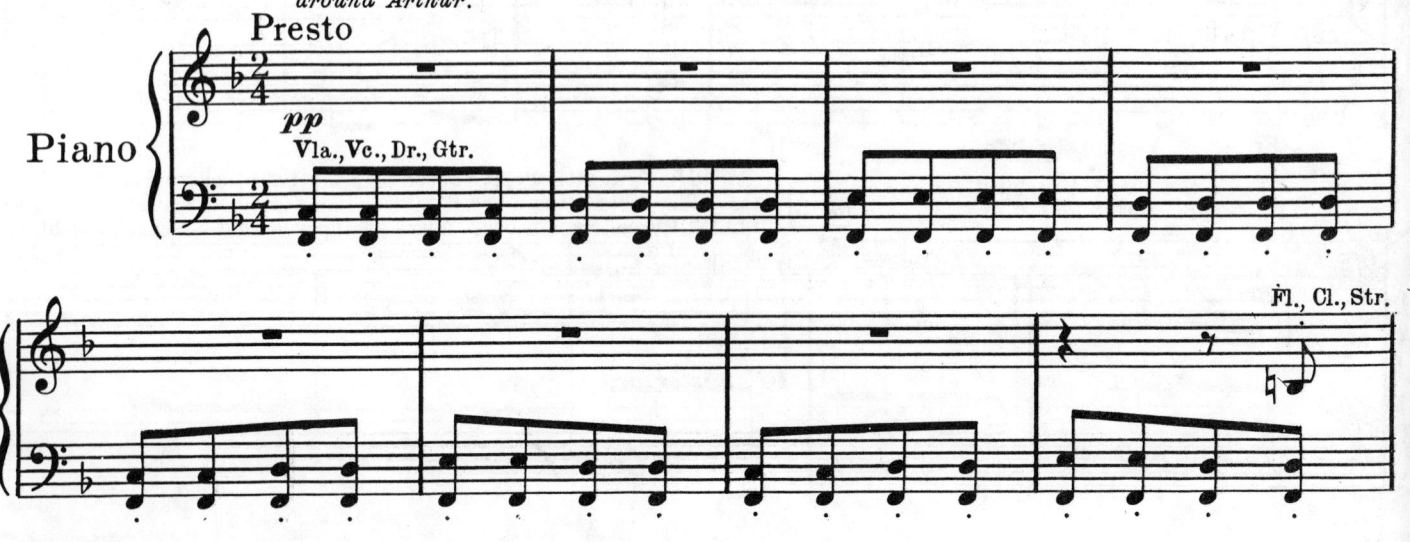

185

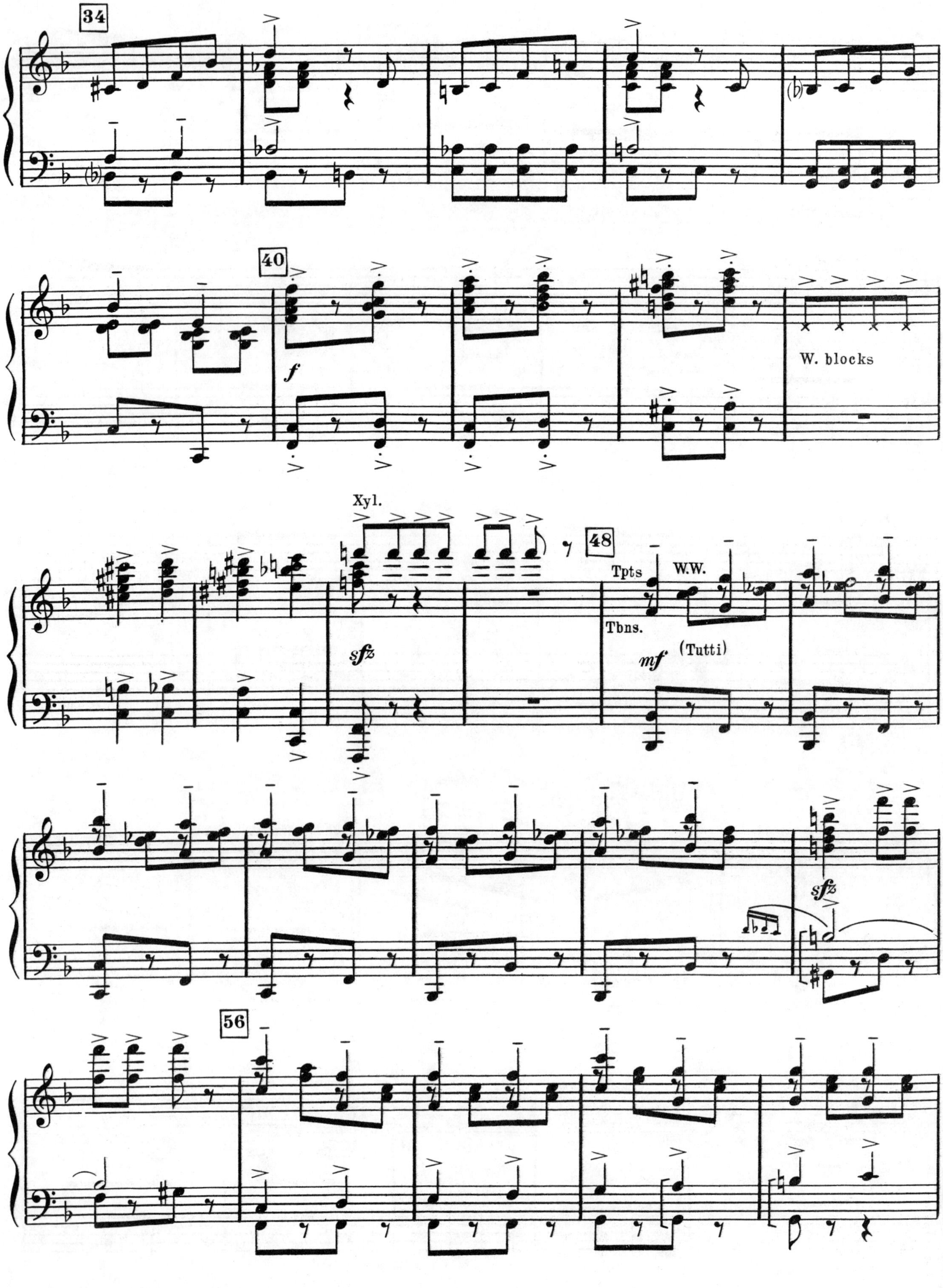
34
40
f
W. blocks
Xyl.
sfz
48
Tpts
W.W.
Tbns.
mf
(Tutti)
sfz
56

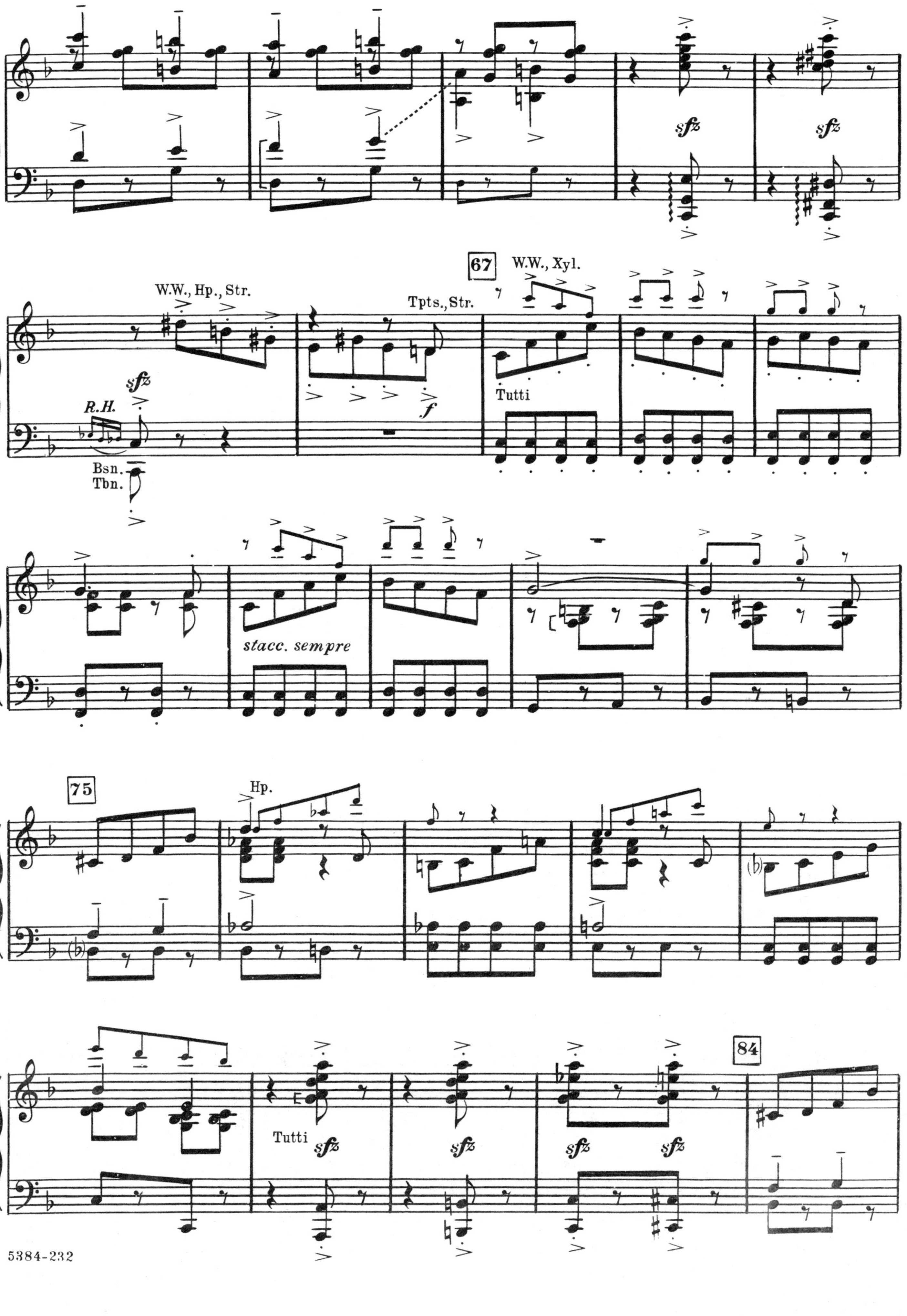
sfz
sfz
67
W.W., Xyl.
W.W., Hp., Str.
Tpts., Str.
sfz
R.H.
f
Tutti
Bsn.
Tbn.
stacc. sempre
75
Hp.
84
Tutti
sfz
sfz
sfz
sfz

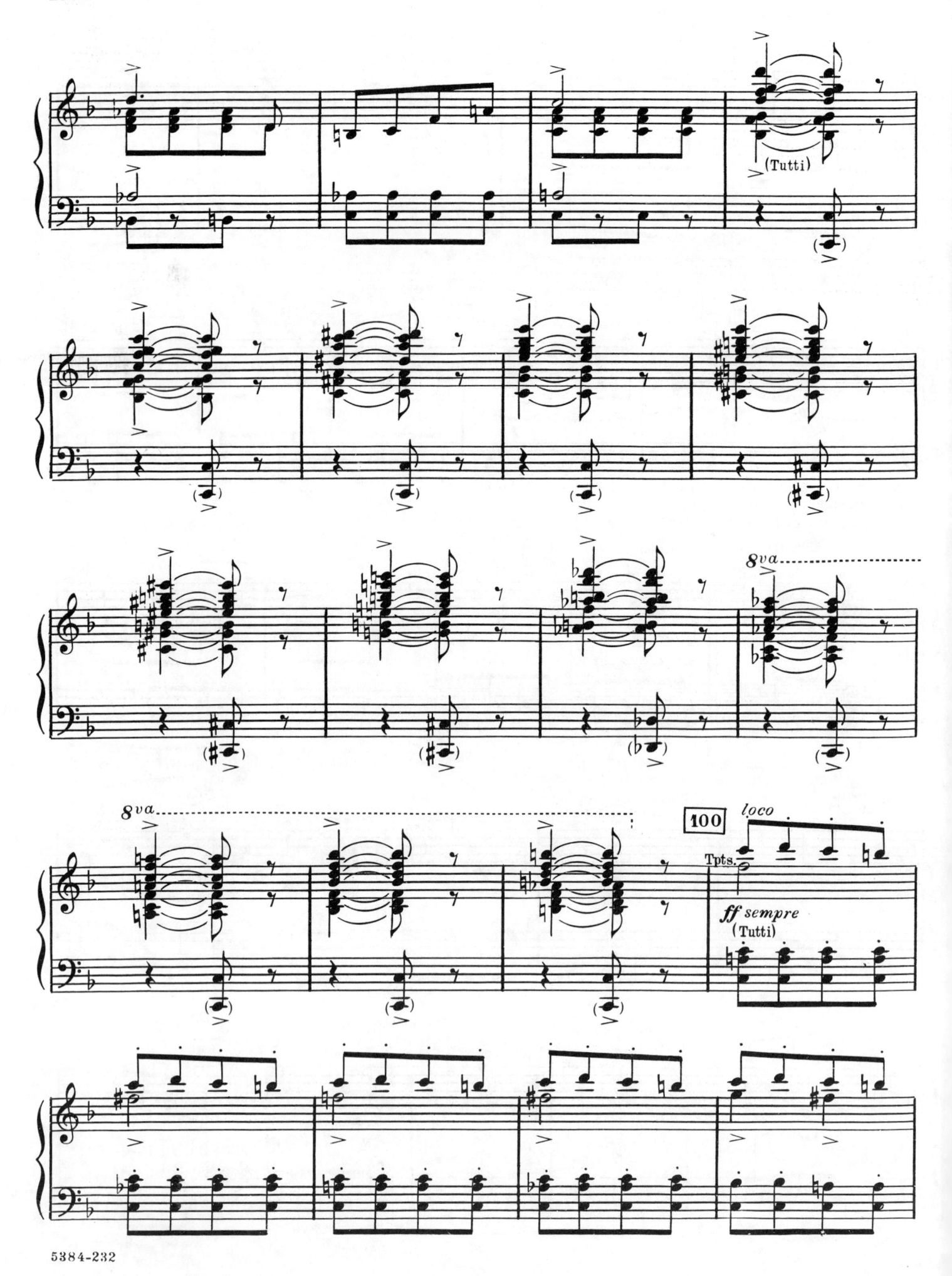
(Tutti)
8va
8va
100
loco
Tpts.
ff sempre
(Tutti)

Morgan and her Court disappear.

(Dialogue)

No. 29   Change Of Scene

Cue: ARTHUR: ... Find Lance. Find Jenny. Tell them to be careful.
    PELLINORE: You know, Arthur?
    ARTHUR: Do as I say, Pelly! *(PELLINORE exits)* Morgan Le Fey!

(The scene changes)

Moderato — Morgan Le Fey! Morgan Le Fey! — Allegro agitato

(The curtain rises.)

FIRST LADY-IN-WAITING:
Goodnight, Milady.

SECOND LADY-IN-WAITING:
Goodnight, Your Majesty.

No. 30 Corridor Scene

190

FIRST LADY-IN-WAITING: Sleep well, Your Majesty.   *LANCELOT appears, looks around furtively and disappears into the Queen's chamber.*

MORDRED appears from the other side, snaps his fingers. Several Knights enter. As he nods to them to follow him, PELLINORE enters. **PELLINORE:** Hey you!   **MORDRED:** The name is Mordred. *(Dialogue continues)*

No. 31 Change Of Scene And Incidental Music

Cue: MORDRED: Pellinore, in a little while, I shall be in charge of this Castle. And shortly after that, gentlemen, the Kingdom. *(Curtain)*

Passionato

Tutti ff

(The curtain rises)

GUENEVERE is seated at her dressing table, brushing her long hair. LANCELOT enters quietly. He looks around and pauses.

192

LANCELOT: Jenny....? *(GUENEVERE rises quickly)* Jenny, I was in the yard...

I couldn't sleep... I saw the light in your window... I knew you were alone... I tried to

stay away... I tried, but I... Jenny, I... *They embrace passionately.*

GUENEVERE: LANCELOT: GUENEVERE:
Did anyone see you?   No one. The castle is dark. I was careful, Jenny, don't be afraid.   But I am afraid.

LANCELOT:
I swear we're alone. No one saw me enter, Jenny, there's nothing to fear. Arthur won't be back until... *(Dialogue continues)*

5384-232

No. 32 I Loved You Once In Silence

Cue: GUENEVERE: ... And suddenly we're less alone than ever.
LANCELOT: But why?
GUENEVERE: *(The music begins.)* Now that the people are gone, can't you see the shadow between us? It's wider than the sea. It fills the room. Perhaps it would have been better if we had never said a word to each other at all. *(She sings)*

I loved you once in silence, And mis-'ry was all I knew. Try-ing so to keep my love from

showing, All the while not knowing You loved me too. Yes, loved me in lonesome silence; Your heart filled with dark despair... Thinking love would flame in you for-

ev-er, And I'd nev-er, nev-er know the flame was there. Then one day we cast a-way our se-cret long-ing; The rag-ing tide we held in-side would hold no more. The si-lence at last was broken!___ We flung wide ___ our pris-on door.___ Ev-'ry joy-ous word of love was spo-ken... And now there's twice as much grief, Twice the strain for us; Twice the des-pair, Twice the pain for us As we had known be-

197

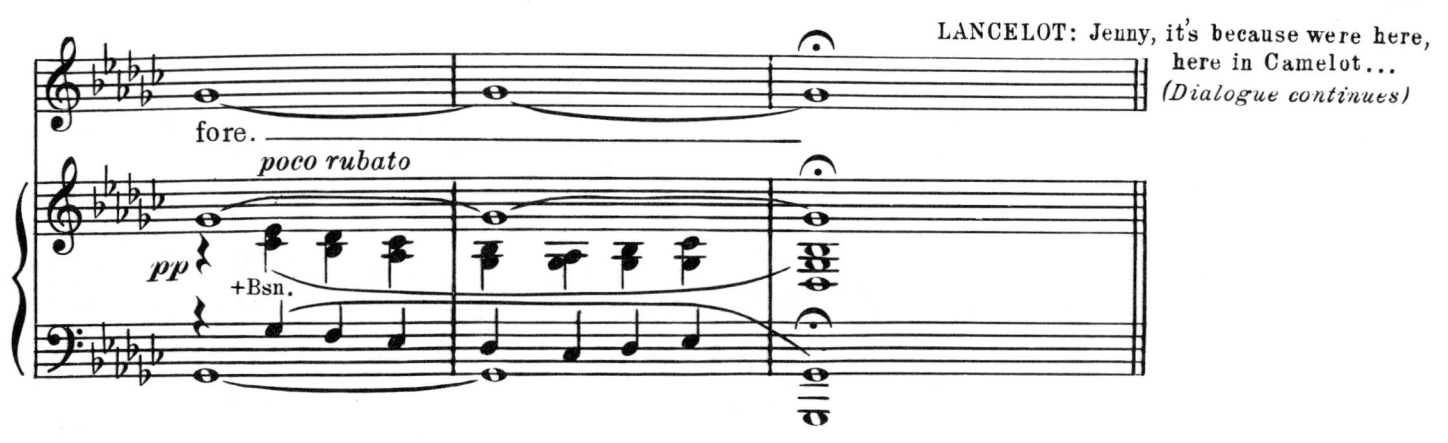

198

We flung wide our pris-on door. Ev-'ry

90 MORDRED and KNIGHTS

joy-ous word of love was spo-ken... And af-ter

tiptoe silently into the room.
Andante

all had been said, Here we are, my love, Si-lent once more And not far, my love...

poco rit
rall.
colla voce

97 (LANCELOT and GUENEVERE embrace) MORDRED:... Lancelot, don't touch your dagger. (LANCELOT whirls around) I accuse you of treason, and order you both to stand trial for your crime. Surrender in the name of the King. (LANCELOT snatches the sword from MORDRED)   Segue

No. 33

Guenevere

199

LANCELOT: If I escape, I shall come and rescue you. If I am killed, send word to Joyous Gard. Someone will come. *(The music begins)*
(He takes a menacing step forward. All stand in tableau — stillness. A chorus enters, wiping out the scene behind.)

Allegro deciso

A MAN: *(stepping forward)*

Out the room, down the hall, Through the yard, to the wall; Slashing fiercely, left and right, Lance es-

Copyright © 1960 (unpub.) & 1962 by Alan Jay Lerner and Frederick Loewe

5384-232

caped them and took flight. On a day, dark and drear, Came to trial Guenevere. Ruled the jury for her shame She be

sen-tenced to the flame. As the

37 dawn filled the sky, On the

day she would die, There was

45 won-der far and near: Would the

ARTHUR enters forlornly.
King burn Gue - ne - vere?
S.
A.
CHORUS: Would the
T.
B.
Would the
Str. (col 8va)
Tpts. 8va
53
King let her die? Would the
King let her die? Would the
Hns.
Br.
Gtr.
Bs.Cl., Bsn.
Gong
King let her die? There was
King let her die? There was

203

61 won-der _____ far and near: _____ Would the

MORDRED enters and looks at the King.

King burn _____ Gue-ne-vere? _____

69 MORDRED: Arthur! What a magnificent dilemma! Let her die, Your life is over; let her live, your life's a fraud. Now which will it be, Arthur?

77
Do you kill the Queen or kill the law?
p sempre
ARTHUR: The jury has ruled. Let justice be done.
ff
Br.
mf
85
CHORUS: She must burn. She must burn,
mf
She must burn. She must burn,
W.W. (col 8va)
p sub.
Br., Str.
Hns.
Spoke the King: She must burn.
Spoke the King: She must burn.

And the mo-ment now was here

And the mo-ment now was here

For the end of Gue-ne-vere.

For the end of Gue-ne-vere.

GUENEVERE enters. She is accompanied by a

109
priest carrying a cross, and soldiers. As she walks
Br.
cresc. sempre
f
across, she pauses near Arthur and looks at him. Their
W.W.
eyes hold a moment, then she continues.
WOMEN:
117
S.
A.
Slow her walk,
bo d her
head,
W.W.
p
Bsn.
Vla.
Vc.
Vls.
To the stake
she was
led...
etc.

125
A HERALD: The Queen is at the stake, Your Majesty.
Tbns.
Shall I signal the torch? (ARTHUR cannot answer) Your Majesty! Your
Tbns.
Majesty!
mp
133
CHORUS: In his grief, so a - lone,
mp
In his 133 grief, so a - lone,
E.H., Bsn.
p sub.
Str., Gtr.
Tbns., Hp., Gong
ARTHUR: I can't!
From the King came a moan...
From the King came a moan...
Cl., Hn.
p

141 I can't! I can't let her die! MORDRED: Well, you're human after all, aren't you, Arthur? Human and helpless.

149 A MAN: Then sud-den-ly earth and sky were dazed by a pound-ing roar;

And sud-den-ly through the dawn an ar-my be-gan to pour,

And lo! Ahead the army, holding aloft his spear, Came Lancelot to save his dear Guenevere.

ARTHUR: Lance! Lance! Come save her. HERALD: Shall I signal the torch, Your Majesty? DINADAN: *(rushing in)* Arthur, an army from Joyous Gard is storming the gate. Shall I double the guard? Arthur, you're inviting a massacre! *(He rushes off)* ARTHUR: Save her, Lance, save her!

By the score _____ fell the dead, _____

By the score _____ fell the dead, _____

As the yard _____ turned to red. _____

As the yard _____ turned to red. _____

Count-less num-bers _____ felt his spear, _____

Count-less num-bers _____ felt his spear, _____

As he res - cued Gue - ne - vere.

As he res - cued Gue - ne - vere.

197 MORDRED: Sweet heaven, what a sight! Can you see it from there Arthur? Can you see your goodly Lancelot murdering your goodly knights? Your table is cracking, Arthur.

205 Can you hear the timbers split? ARTHUR: Merlyn!

Merlyn, make me a hawk. Let me fly away from here.

MORDRED: What a failure you are, **213** Arthur!

How did you think you could survive without

being as ruthless as I? ARTHUR: Merlyn! Merlyn!
Hns.
Tutti cresc.
221
In that dawn, in that gloom,
In that dawn, in that gloom,
221
W.W.
Hp.
gliss.
(Tpts.)
mp Tutti
Tpts.
More than love met its doom.
More than love met its doom.

In the dy - ing can - dle's gleam

In the dy - ing can - dle's gleam

Came the sun - down of a dream.

Came the sun - down of a dream.

DINADAN: (*entering*) Most of the guard is killed, Arthur, and over eighty knights. They're heading for the Channel. I'll make ready the army to follow. Arthur, we want revenge! *(He exits)*

ARTHUR: Oh God, is it all to start again? Is my almighty fling at peace to be over so soon? Am I back where I began? Am I? Am I?

Guenevere, _____ Guene-

Guenevere, _____ Guenevere! In that dim, mournful year, Saw the men she held most dear Go to war for Gue-ne-

217

dear Go to war for Gue - ne -
dear Go to war for Gue - ne -
285
vere! Gue - ne - vere! Gue - ne -
vere! Gue - ne - vere! Gue - ne -
285
ff
vere! Gue - ne - vere!
ff
vere! Gue - ne - vere!
mf sub.

(All but ARTHUR leave as the SCENE CHANGES to the battlefield outside Joyous Gard.)

(LANCELOT followed by GUENEVERE, enters.)

LANCELOT: Jenny— he's here.
(Dialogue continues)

No. 34   Battle Call

Cue: ARTHUR:... Something you cannot taste or touch, smell or feel; without substance, life, reality or memory.

Lento

(Dialogue continues)

No. 35 Farewell

Cue: LANCELOT: Is there nothing to be done?
   ARTHUR: Nothing, but play out the game and leave the decisions to God. Now go.

Andante   (*LANCELOT leaves*)

ARTHUR: You must go, too, Jenny.   GUENEVERE: I know. So often in the past I would look up in your eyes and there I would find forgiveness. Perhaps one day in the future it shall be there again. But I won't be with you....
I won't see it.   (*He takes her in his arms.*)   Oh, Arthur, Arthur, I see what I wanted to see.   ARTHUR: Goodbye, my love... (*GUENEVERE leaves him.*) My dearest love. (*He hears a rustling behind the tent.*) Who's there? (*Dialogue continues.*)

No. 36 Finale Ultimo

221

Cue: ARTHUR: And for as long as you live you will remember what I, the King, tell you; and you will do as I command.
TOM: Yes, Milord.

Allegro moderato

ARTHUR: Each eve-ning from De-cem-ber to De-cem-ber,

Be-fore you drift to sleep up-on your cot,

Think back on all the tales that you re-mem-ber

Of Ca-me-lot.

Ask ev'ry per-son if he's heard the sto-ry,
And tell it strong and clear if he has not:
That once there was a fleet-ing wisp of glo-ry
Called Ca-me-lot.

33
Ca - me - lot!
W.W.
mf
Ca - me - lot!
Hns.
pp
pp
Now say it out with love and joy!
W.W.
Str.
cantando
mp
Hns.
41
TOM:
Ca - me - lot!
W.W.
mf
Ca - me - lot!
(Hns.)
pp
+Tbn.
ARTHUR:
Yes, Ca - me - lot, my boy...
Where
W.W., Str.
mp
mf
pp

once it nev-er rained till af-ter sun-down; By eight a. m. the morn-ing fog had flown. Don't let it be for-got That once there was a spot For one brief shin-ing mo-ment that was known As Ca- me -

67
Andante
My teacher Merlyn, who always remembered things that haven't happened
lot.
Str.
pp
Bsn.
Bass, Timp.
better than things that have, told me once that a few hundred years from now it will be discovered
Cl.
Bs.
that the world is round--- round like the table at which we sat with such high hope and
Tpt. I
75
pp sempre
noble purpose. If you do what I ask, perhaps people will remember how we of
(3 Tpts.)
pp sempre
Camelot went questing for right and honor and justice. Perhaps one day men will sit around
Hn. III
p

this world as we did once at our table and go questing once more... for right... honor... and justice.
83
Ob.
3 Hns.
ritard.
87
PELLINORE: (enters carrying Excalibur) Arthur...?
Tempo Iº
S.
A.
(From a distance)
ARTHUR: Give me the sword.
CHORUS: Ca - me - lot!
T.
B.
Ca - me - lot!
87
Ob.
p sempre
Hns.
W.W.
PELLINORE: Here.
Str.
espr.
Hns.
95
ARTHUR: Kneel, Tom, kneel.
With this sword,
Ca - me - lot!
Ca - me - lot!
95
Str.

Excalibur, I knight you Sir Tom of Warwick. And I command you to return home and carry out my orders. TOM: Yes, Milord. PELLINORE: Now, come, Arthur. You have a battle to fight.

Ca - me - lot! ____
Ca - me - lot! ____

ARTHUR: Battle? I've won my battle, Pelly. Here's my victory! What we did will be remembered.

Ca - me - lot! ____ Don't let it be for -
Ca - me - lot! ____ Don't let it be for -
Ca - me - lot! ____ Don't let it be for -
Ca - me - lot! ____ Don't let it be for -
Ca - me - lot! ____ Don't let it be for -

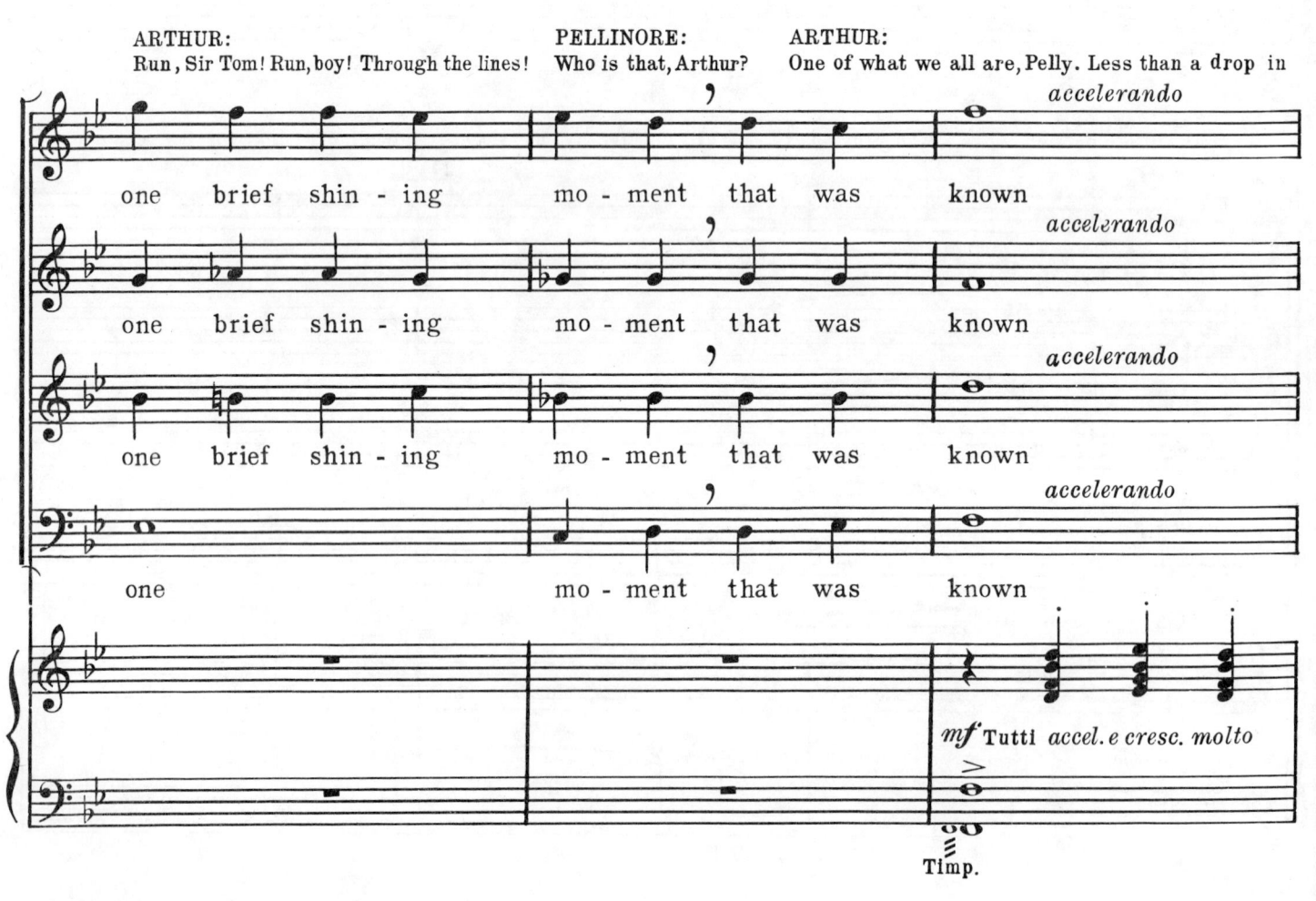

You'll see, Pelly. Now, run, Sir Tom! Behind the lines.   **TOM:** Yes, Milord. *(He runs off)*

got — That once there was a spot — For one brief shin-ing mo-ment that was known

ARTHUR: Run, Sir Tom! Run, boy! Through the lines!   **PELLINORE:** Who is that, Arthur?   **ARTHUR:** One of what we all are, Pelly. Less than a drop in the great blue motion of the sunlit sea. But it seems some of the drops sparkle, Pelly. Some of them do sparkle!

Largo

(The curtain falls slowly)

No. 37 Music For Curtain Calls And Exit

231

41
Tpts.,Tbns.
W.W., Str.
49
Tutti
Bsn.,Hns. 8va
57
Bsn.,Tbn.
63
Str.
poco rit.
W.W., Tpts.

67
Tutti
W.W., Tpts.
Hns.
Tutti
rall.
Meno mosso
Ob., Bsn., Str.
f cantabile
76
W.W., Tpts., Bells, Hp.
+Hns.
W.W.
Br.
Hns.
84
W.W., Str.

W.W., Hns., Str.,
Bells, Hp.
Fl., Ob., Str.
92
+Bsn., Hns., Bells
Ped.
*
+Tbn. I
W.W., Tpts., Str.
100
Tbns.
Hns.
Hns., Tbns.
Fl., Ob.,
Tpt. I, Str.
rall.
Tutti
(Hns)
Allegro
Br., Str., Xyl.
f
+W.W.
f Tpts.
Tbns.

Giocoso
110
W.W., Bells, Str.
W.W., Bells, Vls.
Hns.
Tbns.
118
Hns. Str.
W.W., Vls.
+Tpts.
Hns., Tbns.
Ob.
Vls., Vla.
126
Fl. 8va
Hns.

134
+Tpts.
W.W., Str.
Bells
Tutti
W.W., Str
Tpts.
Tbns.
Hns.
Tbns.
147
Tutti
Hns.
f sempre
(Br.)
Poco maestoso
Hp.
gliss.
ff
fff
Timp.

M1503
.L818
C3
1962

8118 X

M1503
.L818
C3
1962